Sunrise

TBI Journal

ABELLO, KRISTIN, Author
SUNRISE JOURNAL
KRISTIN ABELLO

Published by:
ELITE ONLINE PUBLISHING
63 East 11400 South #230
Sandy, UT 84070
EliteOnlinePublishing.com

ISBN: 978-1-956642-36-0

HEA039110

QUANTITY PURCHASES: Schools, companies, professional groups, clubs, and other organizations may qualify for special terms when ordering quantities of this title. For information, email
info@eliteonlinepublishing.com

Dear Friend,

The Sunrise Journal was prayerfully and wholeheartedly created for the TBI Community. This is somewhere for the patient and/or caregiver to go to record their progress.

My hope to all, that this can be a safe place to serve you daily inspirational reminders, during your personal healing journey.

Enjoy!
XO,
Kristin Abello

Visit **KristinAbello.com**
to buy the book

Sunrise:
Life after Traumatic Brain Injury:
A Healing Journey
in Surviving TBI,
An Empowering True Story

Sunrise

TBI Journal

Date: _____

With God, all things are possible
—Matthew 19:26

I am grateful for ...

☼ _____
☼ _____
☼ _____

Positive Affirmations

☼ _____
☼ _____
☼ _____

Did you meditate? ☐ yes ☐ no
(At least 5 minutes, a great meditation APP: Calm.com)

Did you do the following?

Physical Therapy ☐ yes ☐ no
Occupational Therapy ☐ yes ☐ no
Speech Therapy ☐ yes ☐ no
Music Therapy ☐ yes ☐ no
Equine Therapy ☐ yes ☐ no
Cognitive Behavior Therapy ☐ yes ☐ no

How did you feel?

☐ awesome ☐ okay ☐ not so good

Did you get a breath of Fresh Air Today?

☐ yes ☐ no

Did you get your healthy 7-9 hrs of sleep?

☐ yes ☐ no

Naps:

☐ 1-2 hours ☐ 2-4 hours ☐ other

Listening to music

Listening to music you love will make your brain release more dopamine! The naturally occurring happy chemical. Make sure to listen to more of your favorite tunes!

Meals Today:

Be sure to add
Functional Foods in your diet

Breakfast
_____
_____

Snack
_____
_____

Lunch
_____
_____

Snack
_____
_____

Dinner
_____
_____

Snack
_____
_____
_____

Did you Spice up your day with Turmeric? ☐ yes ☐ no

(Best for Neuroprotection)

Did you get your Rainbow Greens today? ☐ yes ☐ no

(Dark Leafy Green is best for Brain Health)

Did you get Nuts/Seeds today? ☐ yes ☐ no

Vitamins I took today _____

(Omega-3 Fatty Acid is best for Your Brain Power and keeping your brain healthy.)
Great Sources of Omega-3s: *Salmon, Oysters, Caviar, Flax Seeds, Chia Seeds, and Walnuts.*
Other Great Sources of Brain Power - *Vitamins: B1, B6, B12, C, E, Antioxidants, Beta Carotene and Probiotics.*

Reminder: Cinnamon and Rosemary are great for neurological benefits.

Daily Exercise:

*If you are at the Beginning of your brain injury recovery, 5 minutes is great on the recumbent bike. OR if you are further along in recovery, a walk, weight bearing exercise and yoga are great choices. Remember not too much. Start slow and build up to 20 minutes. *Consult with your Dr for your proper exercise prescription.*

Exercise Log:

_____
_____
_____
_____
_____

Did you get your Yoga stillness today? ☐ yes ☐ no

This is your gateway to mental clarity and spiritual calm. Based on a centuries-old and scientifically proven pathway to health, Yoga is a gold star to your success. Great resources: Glo.com and Asanarebel.com

Daily Reflection:

Date: _____

Keep your face always toward the sunshine and
shadows will fall behind you.
– Walt Whitman

I am grateful for ...

☼ _____

☼ _____

☼ _____

Positive Affirmations

☼ _____

☼ _____

☼ _____

Did you meditate? ☐ yes ☐ no
(At least 5 minutes, a great meditation APP: Calm.com)

Did you do the following?

Physical Therapy   ☐ yes ☐ no

Occupational Therapy   ☐ yes ☐ no

Speech Therapy   ☐ yes ☐ no

Music Therapy   ☐ yes ☐ no

Equine Therapy   ☐ yes ☐ no

Cognitive Behavior Therapy ☐ yes ☐ no

How did you feel?

☐ awesome ☐ okay ☐ not so good

Did you get a breath of Fresh Air Today?

☐ yes   ☐ no

Did you get your healthy 7-9 hrs of sleep?

☐ yes   ☐ no

Naps:

☐ 1-2 hours ☐ 2-4 hours ☐ other

Listening to music

Listening to music you love will make your brain release more dopamine! The naturally occurring happy chemical. Make sure to listen to more of your favorite tunes!

Meals Today:

Be sure to add
Functional Foods in your diet

Breakfast
_____

_____

Snack
_____

_____

Lunch
_____

_____

Snack
_____

_____

Dinner
_____

_____

Snack
_____

_____

Did you Spice up your day with Turmeric?　☐ yes　☐ no

(Best for Neuroprotection)

Did you get your Rainbow Greens today?　☐ yes　☐ no

(Dark Leafy Green is best for Brain Health)

Did you get Nuts/Seeds today?　☐ yes　☐ no

Vitamins I took today _____

(Omega-3 Fatty Acid is best for Your Brain Power and keeping your brain healthy.)
Great Sources of Omega-3s: *Salmon, Oysters, Caviar, Flax Seeds, Chia Seeds, and Walnuts.*
Other Great Sources of Brain Power – *Vitamins: B1, B6, B12, C, E, Antioxidants, Beta Carotene and Probiotics.*

Reminder: Cinnamon and Rosemary are great for neurological benefits.

Daily Exercise:

If you are at the Beginning of your brain injury recovery, 5 minutes is great on the recumbent bike. OR if you are further along in recovery, a walk, weight bearing exercise and yoga are great choices. Remember not too much. Start slow and build up to 20 minutes. *Consult with your Dr for your proper exercise prescription.

Exercise Log:

_____

_____

_____

_____

Did you get your Yoga stillness today?　☐ yes　☐ no

This is your gateway to mental clarity and spiritual calm. Based on a centuries-old and scientifically proven pathway to health, Yoga is a gold star to your success. Great resources: Glo.com and Asanarebel.com

Daily Reflection:

Date: _____

I am grateful for ...

☀ _____
☀ _____
☀ _____

Did you meditate?   ☐ yes   ☐ no
(At least 5 minutes, a great meditation APP: Calm.com)

Did you do the following?

Physical Therapy ☐ yes ☐ no
Occupational Therapy ☐ yes ☐ no
Speech Therapy ☐ yes ☐ no
Music Therapy ☐ yes ☐ no
Equine Therapy ☐ yes ☐ no
Cognitive Behavior Therapy ☐ yes ☐ no

How did you feel?
☐ awesome   ☐ okay   ☐ not so good

Did you get a breath of Fresh Air Today?
☐ yes   ☐ no

Did you get your healthy 7-9 hrs of sleep?
☐ yes   ☐ no

Naps:
☐ 1-2 hours   ☐ 2-4 hours   ☐ other

Positive Affirmations

☀ _____
☀ _____
☀ _____

Listening to music
Listening to music you love will make your brain release more dopamine! The naturally occurring happy chemical. Make sure to listen to more of your favorite tunes!

Meals Today:
Be sure to add
Functional Foods in your diet

Breakfast
_____

Snack
_____

Lunch
_____

Snack
_____

Dinner
_____

Snack
_____

Did you Spice up your day with Turmeric?   ☐ yes   ☐ no

(Best for Neuroprotection)

Did you get your Rainbow Greens today?   ☐ yes   ☐ no

(Dark Leafy Green is best for Brain Health)

Did you get Nuts/Seeds today?   ☐ yes   ☐ no

Vitamins I took today _____

(Omega-3 Fatty Acid is best for Your Brain Power and keeping your brain healthy.)
Great Sources of Omega-3s: *Salmon, Oysters, Caviar, Flax Seeds, Chia Seeds, and Walnuts.*
Other Great Sources of Brain Power *- Vitamins: B1, B6, B12, C, E, Antioxidants, Beta Carotene and Probiotics.*

Reminder: Cinnamon and Rosemary are great for neurological benefits.

Daily Exercise:

*If you are at the Beginning of your brain injury recovery, 5 minutes is great on the recumbent bike. OR if you are further along in recovery, a walk, weight bearing exercise and yoga are great choices. Remember not too much. Start slow and build up to 20 minutes. *Consult with your Dr for your proper exercise prescription.*

Exercise Log:

_____

_____

_____

_____

Did you get your Yoga stillness today?   ☐ yes   ☐ no

This is your gateway to mental clarity and spiritual calm. Based on a centuries-old and scientifically proven pathway to health, Yoga is a gold star to your success. Great resources: Glo.com and Asanarebel.com

Daily Reflection:

Date: _____

I am grateful for ...

- ○ _____
- ○ _____
- ○ _____

Positive Affirmations

- ○ _____
- ○ _____
- ○ _____

Did you meditate?   ☐ yes   ☐ no

(At least 5 minutes, a great meditation APP: Calm.com)

Did you do the following?

Physical Therapy	☐ yes	☐ no
Occupational Therapy	☐ yes	☐ no
Speech Therapy	☐ yes	☐ no
Music Therapy	☐ yes	☐ no
Equine Therapy	☐ yes	☐ no
Cognitive Behavior Therapy	☐ yes	☐ no

How did you feel?

☐ awesome   ☐ okay   ☐ not so good

Did you get a breath of Fresh Air Today?

☐ yes   ☐ no

Did you get your healthy 7-9 hrs of sleep?

☐ yes   ☐ no

Naps:

☐ 1-2 hours   ☐ 2-4 hours   ☐ other

Listening to music

Listening to music you love will make your brain release more dopamine! The naturally occurring happy chemical. Make sure to listen to more of your favorite tunes!

Meals Today:

Be sure to add Functional Foods in your diet

Breakfast
_____
_____

Snack
_____
_____

Lunch
_____
_____

Snack
_____
_____

Dinner
_____
_____

Snack
_____
_____

Did you Spice up your day with Turmeric?　　　☐ yes　☐ no

(Best for Neuroprotection)

Did you get your Rainbow Greens today?　　　☐ yes　☐ no

(Dark Leafy Green is best for Brain Health)

Did you get Nuts/Seeds today?　　　☐ yes　☐ no

Vitamins I took today _____

(Omega-3 Fatty Acid is best for Your Brain Power and keeping your brain healthy.)
Great Sources of Omega-3s: *Salmon, Oysters, Caviar, Flax Seeds, Chia Seeds, and Walnuts.*
Other Great Sources of Brain Power – *Vitamins: B1, B6, B12, C, E, Antioxidants, Beta Carotene and Probiotics.*

Reminder: Cinnamon and Rosemary are great for neurological benefits.

Daily Exercise:

*If you are at the Beginning of your brain injury recovery, 5 minutes is great on the recumbent bike. OR if you are further along in recovery, a walk, weight bearing exercise and yoga are great choices. Remember not too much. Start slow and build up to 20 minutes. *Consult with your Dr for your proper exercise prescription.*

Exercise Log:

_____

_____

_____

_____

Did you get your Yoga stillness today?　　　☐ yes　☐ no

This is your gateway to mental clarity and spiritual calm. Based on a centuries-old and scientifically proven pathway to health, Yoga is a gold star to your success. Great resources: Glo.com and Asanarebel.com

Daily Reflection:

Date: _____

I am grateful for ...

☼ _____

☼ _____

☼ _____

Positive Affirmations

☼ _____

☼ _____

☼ _____

Did you meditate? ☐ yes ☐ no
(At least 5 minutes, a great meditation APP: Calm.com)

Did you do the following?

Physical Therapy ☐ yes ☐ no

Occupational Therapy ☐ yes ☐ no

Speech Therapy ☐ yes ☐ no

Music Therapy ☐ yes ☐ no

Equine Therapy ☐ yes ☐ no

Cognitive Behavior Therapy ☐ yes ☐ no

How did you feel?

☐ *awesome* ☐ *okay* ☐ *not so good*

Did you get a breath of Fresh Air Today?

☐ *yes* ☐ *no*

Did you get your healthy 7-9 hrs of sleep?

☐ *yes* ☐ *no*

Naps:

☐ *1-2 hours* ☐ *2-4 hours* ☐ *other*

Listening to music

Listening to music you love will make your brain release more dopamine! The naturally occurring happy chemical. Make sure to listen to more of your favorite tunes!

Meals Today:

Be sure to add
Functional Foods in your diet

Breakfast
_____

_____

Snack
_____

_____

Lunch
_____

_____

Snack
_____

_____

Dinner
_____

_____

Snack
_____

_____

Did you Spice up your day with Turmeric? ☐ yes ☐ no
(Best for Neuroprotection)

Did you get your Rainbow Greens today? ☐ yes ☐ no
(Dark Leafy Green is best for Brain Health)

Did you get Nuts/Seeds today? ☐ yes ☐ no

Vitamins I took today _____

(Omega-3 Fatty Acid is best for Your Brain Power and keeping your brain healthy.)
Great Sources of Omega-3s: *Salmon, Oysters, Caviar, Flax Seeds, Chia Seeds, and Walnuts.*
Other Great Sources of Brain Power - *Vitamins: B1, B6, B12, C, E, Antioxidants, Beta Carotene and Probiotics.*

> *Reminder: Cinnamon and Rosemary are great for neurological benefits.*

Daily Exercise:

If you are at the Beginning of your brain injury recovery, 5 minutes is great on the recumbent bike. OR if you are further along in recovery, a walk, weight bearing exercise and yoga are great choices. Remember not too much. Start slow and build up to 20 minutes. *Consult with your Dr for your proper exercise prescription.

Exercise Log:
_____
_____
_____
_____
_____

Did you get your Yoga stillness today? ☐ yes ☐ no

This is your gateway to mental clarity and spiritual calm. Based on a centuries-old and scientifically proven pathway to health, Yoga is a gold star to your success. Great resources: Glo.com and Asanarebel.com

Daily Reflection:

Date: _____

Repeat after me "I can do this."
- Traumatic Brain Injury Awareness

I am grateful for ...

○ _____

○ _____

○ _____

Positive Affirmations

○ _____

○ _____

○ _____

Did you meditate? ☐ yes ☐ no

(At least 5 minutes, a great meditation APP: Calm.com)

Did you do the following?

Physical Therapy ☐ yes ☐ no

Occupational Therapy ☐ yes ☐ no

Speech Therapy ☐ yes ☐ no

Music Therapy ☐ yes ☐ no

Equine Therapy ☐ yes ☐ no

Cognitive Behavior Therapy ☐ yes ☐ no

How did you feel?

☐ awesome ☐ okay ☐ not so good

Did you get a breath of Fresh Air Today?

☐ yes ☐ no

Did you get your healthy 7-9 hrs of sleep?

☐ yes ☐ no

Naps:

☐ 1-2 hours ☐ 2-4 hours ☐ other

Listening to music

Listening to music you love will make your brain release more dopamine! The naturally occurring happy chemical. Make sure to listen to more of your favorite tunes!

Meals Today:

Be sure to add Functional Foods in your diet

Breakfast
_____
_____

Snack
_____
_____

Lunch
_____
_____

Snack
_____
_____

Dinner
_____
_____

Snack
_____
_____

Did you Spice up your day with Turmeric?   ☐ yes   ☐ no
(Best for Neuroprotection)

Did you get your Rainbow Greens today?   ☐ yes   ☐ no
(Dark Leafy Green is best for Brain Health)

Did you get Nuts/Seeds today?   ☐ yes   ☐ no

Vitamins I took today _____

(Omega-3 Fatty Acid is best for Your Brain Power and keeping your brain healthy.)
Great Sources of Omega-3s: *Salmon, Oysters, Caviar, Flax Seeds, Chia Seeds, and Walnuts.*
Other Great Sources of Brain Power - *Vitamins: B1, B6, B12, C, E, Antioxidants, Beta Carotene and Probiotics.*

Reminder: Cinnamon and Rosemary are great for neurological benefits.

Daily Exercise:

If you are at the Beginning of your brain injury recovery, 5 minutes is great on the recumbent bike. OR if you are further along in recovery, a walk, weight bearing exercise and yoga are great choices. Remember not too much. Start slow and build up to 20 minutes. *Consult with your Dr for your proper exercise prescription.

Exercise Log:
_____
_____
_____
_____
_____

Did you get your Yoga stillness today?   ☐ yes   ☐ no

This is your gateway to mental clarity and spiritual calm. Based on a centuries-old and scientifically proven pathway to health, Yoga is a gold star to your success. Great resources: Glo.com and Asanarebel.com

Daily Reflection:

Date: _____

Write it on your heart that every day is
the best day in the year.
– Ralph Waldo Emerson

I am grateful for ...

☼ _____

☼ _____

☼ _____

Positive Affirmations

☼ _____

☼ _____

☼ _____

Did you meditate?　☐ *yes*　☐ *no*
(At least 5 minutes, a great meditation APP: Calm.com)

Did you do the following?

Physical Therapy　☐ *yes*　☐ *no*

Occupational Therapy　☐ *yes*　☐ *no*

Speech Therapy　☐ *yes*　☐ *no*

Music Therapy　☐ *yes*　☐ *no*

Equine Therapy　☐ *yes*　☐ *no*

Cognitive Behavior Therapy　☐ *yes*　☐ *no*

How did you feel?

☐ *awesome*　☐ *okay*　☐ *not so good*

Did you get a breath of Fresh Air Today?

☐ *yes*　☐ *no*

Did you get your healthy 7–9 hrs of sleep?

☐ *yes*　☐ *no*

Naps:

☐ *1-2 hours*　☐ *2-4 hours*　☐ *other*

Listening to music

Listening to music you love will make your brain release more dopamine! The naturally occurring happy chemical. Make sure to listen to more of your favorite tunes!

Meals Today:

Be sure to add
Functional Foods in your diet

Breakfast
_____

Snack
_____

Lunch
_____

Snack
_____

Dinner
_____

Snack
_____

Did you Spice up your day with Turmeric? ☐ yes ☐ no

(Best for Neuroprotection)

Did you get your Rainbow Greens today? ☐ yes ☐ no

(Dark Leafy Green is best for Brain Health)

Did you get Nuts/Seeds today? ☐ yes ☐ no

Vitamins I took today _____

(Omega-3 Fatty Acid is best for Your Brain Power and keeping your brain healthy.)
Great Sources of Omega-3s: *Salmon, Oysters, Caviar, Flax Seeds, Chia Seeds, and Walnuts.*
Other Great Sources of Brain Power – *Vitamins: B1, B6, B12, C, E, Antioxidants, Beta Carotene and Probiotics.*

Reminder: Cinnamon and Rosemary are great for neurological benefits.

Daily Exercise:

If you are at the Beginning of your brain injury recovery, 5 minutes is great on the recumbent bike. OR if you are further along in recovery, a walk, weight bearing exercise and yoga are great choices. Remember not too much. Start slow and build up to 20 minutes. *Consult with your Dr for your proper exercise prescription.

Exercise Log:

_____

_____

_____

_____

Did you get your Yoga stillness today? ☐ yes ☐ no

This is your gateway to mental clarity and spiritual calm. Based on a centuries-old and scientifically proven pathway to health, Yoga is a gold star to your success. Great resources: Glo.com and Asanarebel.com

Daily Reflection:

Date: _____

*Do ordinary things with
extraordinary love.
– Mother Teresa*

I am grateful for ...

☼ _____
☼ _____
☼ _____

Positive Affirmations

☼ _____
☼ _____
☼ _____

Did you meditate? ☐ yes ☐ no

(At least 5 minutes, a great meditation APP: Calm.com)

Did you do the following?

Physical Therapy   ☐ yes ☐ no
Occupational Therapy   ☐ yes ☐ no
Speech Therapy   ☐ yes ☐ no
Music Therapy   ☐ yes ☐ no
Equine Therapy   ☐ yes ☐ no
Cognitive Behavior Therapy ☐ yes ☐ no

How did you feel?

☐ awesome   ☐ okay   ☐ not so good

Did you get a breath of Fresh Air Today?

☐ yes   ☐ no

Did you get your healthy 7-9 hrs of sleep?

☐ yes   ☐ no

Naps:

☐ 1-2 hours ☐ 2-4 hours ☐ other

Listening to music

*Listening to music you love will make your
brain release more dopamine! The
naturally occurring happy chemical.
Make sure to listen to more of your favorite
tunes!*

Meals Today:

*Be sure to add
Functional Foods in your diet*

Breakfast _____

_____

Snack _____

_____

Lunch _____

_____

Snack _____

_____

Dinner _____

_____

Snack _____

_____

Did you Spice up your day with Turmeric? ☐ yes ☐ no

(Best for Neuroprotection)

Did you get your Rainbow Greens today? ☐ yes ☐ no

(Dark Leafy Green is best for Brain Health)

Did you get Nuts/Seeds today? ☐ yes ☐ no

Vitamins I took today _____

(Omega-3 Fatty Acid is best for Your Brain Power and keeping your brain healthy.)
Great Sources of Omega-3s: *Salmon, Oysters, Caviar, Flax Seeds, Chia Seeds, and Walnuts.*
Other Great Sources of Brain Power - *Vitamins: B1, B6, B12, C, E, Antioxidants, Beta Carotene and Probiotics.*

Reminder: Cinnamon and Rosemary are great for neurological benefits.

Daily Exercise:

If you are at the Beginning of your brain injury recovery, 5 minutes is great on the recumbent bike. OR if you are further along in recovery, a walk, weight bearing exercise and yoga are great choices. Remember not too much. Start slow and build up to 20 minutes. *Consult with your Dr for your proper exercise prescription.

Exercise Log:

_____

_____

_____

_____

Did you get your Yoga stillness today? ☐ yes ☐ no

This is your gateway to mental clarity and spiritual calm. Based on a centuries-old and scientifically proven pathway to health, Yoga is a gold star to your success. Great resources: Glo.com and Asanarebel.com

Daily Reflection:

Date: _____

You can, you should, and if you're brave
enough to start, YOU WILL.
- Stephen King

I am grateful for ...

◌ _____

◌ _____

◌ _____

Positive Affirmations

◌ _____

◌ _____

◌ _____

Did you meditate?   ☐ yes   ☐ no

(At least 5 minutes, a great meditation APP: Calm.com)

Did you do the following?

Physical Therapy   ☐ yes   ☐ no

Occupational Therapy   ☐ yes   ☐ no

Speech Therapy   ☐ yes   ☐ no

Music Therapy   ☐ yes   ☐ no

Equine Therapy   ☐ yes   ☐ no

Cognitive Behavior Therapy ☐ yes   ☐ no

How did you feel?

☐ *awesome*   ☐ *okay*   ☐ *not so good*

Did you get a breath of Fresh Air Today?

☐ *yes*   ☐ *no*

Did you get your healthy 7-9 hrs of sleep?

☐ *yes*   ☐ *no*

Naps:

☐ *1-2 hours*   ☐ *2-4 hours*   ☐ *other*

Listening to music

Listening to music you love will make your brain release more dopamine! The naturally occurring happy chemical. Make sure to listen to more of your favorite tunes!

Meals Today:

Be sure to add
Functional Foods in your diet

Breakfast
_____
_____

Snack
_____
_____

Lunch
_____
_____

Snack
_____
_____

Dinner
_____
_____

Snack
_____
_____

Did you Spice up your day with Turmeric?   ☐ yes   ☐ no

(Best for Neuroprotection)

Did you get your Rainbow Greens today?   ☐ yes   ☐ no

(Dark Leafy Green is best for Brain Health)

Did you get Nuts/Seeds today?   ☐ yes   ☐ no

Vitamins I took today _____

(Omega-3 Fatty Acid is best for Your Brain Power and keeping your brain healthy.)
Great Sources of Omega-3s: *Salmon, Oysters, Caviar, Flax Seeds, Chia Seeds, and Walnuts.*
Other Great Sources of Brain Power – *Vitamins: B1, B6, B12, C, E, Antioxidants, Beta Carotene and Probiotics.*

Reminder: Cinnamon and Rosemary are great for neurological benefits.

Daily Exercise:

*If you are at the Beginning of your brain injury recovery, 5 minutes is great on the recumbent bike. OR if you are further along in recovery, a walk, weight bearing exercise and yoga are great choices. Remember not too much. Start slow and build up to 20 minutes. *Consult with your Dr for your proper exercise prescription.*

Exercise Log:

_____

_____

_____

_____

Did you get your Yoga stillness today?   ☐ yes   ☐ no

This is your gateway to mental clarity and spiritual calm. Based on a centuries-old and scientifically proven pathway to health, Yoga is a gold star to your success. Great resources: Glo.com and Asanarebel.com

Daily Reflection:

Date: _____

I am grateful for …

- ☼ _____
- ☼ _____
- ☼ _____

Positive Affirmations

- ☼ _____
- ☼ _____
- ☼ _____

Did you meditate?   ☐ yes   ☐ no
(At least 5 minutes, a great meditation APP: Calm.com)

Did you do the following?

Physical Therapy	☐ yes	☐ no
Occupational Therapy	☐ yes	☐ no
Speech Therapy	☐ yes	☐ no
Music Therapy	☐ yes	☐ no
Equine Therapy	☐ yes	☐ no
Cognitive Behavior Therapy	☐ yes	☐ no

How did you feel?
☐ awesome   ☐ okay   ☐ not so good

Did you get a breath of Fresh Air Today?
☐ yes   ☐ no

Did you get your healthy 7-9 hrs of sleep?
☐ yes   ☐ no

Naps:
☐ 1-2 hours   ☐ 2-4 hours   ☐ other

Listening to music
Listening to music you love will make your brain release more dopamine! The naturally occurring happy chemical. Make sure to listen to more of your favorite tunes!

Meals Today:
Be sure to add Functional Foods in your diet

Breakfast
_____
_____

Snack
_____
_____

Lunch
_____
_____

Snack
_____
_____

Dinner
_____
_____

Snack
_____
_____

Did you Spice up your day with Turmeric? ☐ yes ☐ no

(Best for Neuroprotection)

Did you get your Rainbow Greens today? ☐ yes ☐ no

(Dark Leafy Green is best for Brain Health)

Did you get Nuts/Seeds today? ☐ yes ☐ no

Vitamins I took today _____

(Omega-3 Fatty Acid is best for Your Brain Power and keeping your brain healthy.)
Great Sources of Omega-3s: *Salmon, Oysters, Caviar, Flax Seeds, Chia Seeds, and Walnuts.*
Other Great Sources of Brain Power – *Vitamins: B1, B6, B12, C, E, Antioxidants, Beta Carotene and Probiotics.*

Reminder: Cinnamon and Rosemary are great for neurological benefits.

Daily Exercise:

If you are at the Beginning of your brain injury recovery, 5 minutes is great on the recumbent bike. OR if you are further along in recovery, a walk, weight bearing exercise and yoga are great choices. Remember not too much. Start slow and build up to 20 minutes. *Consult with your Dr for your proper exercise prescription.

Exercise Log:

_____

_____

_____

_____

Did you get your Yoga stillness today? ☐ yes ☐ no

This is your gateway to mental clarity and spiritual calm. Based on a centuries-old and scientifically proven pathway to health, Yoga is a gold star to your success. Great resources: Glo.com and Asanarebel.com

Daily Reflection:

Date: _____

> *The only person you are destined to
> become is the person you decide to be.*
> *– Ralph Waldo Emerson*

I am grateful for ...

 _____

_____

_____

Positive Affirmations

_____

_____

_____

Did you meditate?   ☐ yes   ☐ no
(At least 5 minutes, a great meditation APP: Calm.com)

Did you do the following?

Physical Therapy   ☐ yes   ☐ no

Occupational Therapy   ☐ yes   ☐ no

Speech Therapy   ☐ yes   ☐ no

Music Therapy   ☐ yes   ☐ no

Equine Therapy   ☐ yes   ☐ no

Cognitive Behavior Therapy ☐ yes   ☐ no

How did you feel?

☐ awesome   ☐ okay   ☐ not so good

Did you get a breath of Fresh Air Today?

☐ yes   ☐ no

Did you get your healthy 7-9 hrs of sleep?

☐ yes   ☐ no

Naps:

☐ 1-2 hours   ☐ 2-4 hours   ☐ other

Listening to music
Listening to music you love will make your brain release more dopamine! The naturally occurring happy chemical. Make sure to listen to more of your favorite tunes!

Meals Today:
*Be sure to add
Functional Foods in your diet*

Breakfast
_____

Snack
_____

Lunch
_____

Snack
_____

Dinner
_____

Snack
_____

Did you Spice up your day with Turmeric? ☐ yes ☐ no
(Best for Neuroprotection)

Did you get your Rainbow Greens today? ☐ yes ☐ no
(Dark Leafy Green is best for Brain Health)

Did you get Nuts/Seeds today? ☐ yes ☐ no

Vitamins I took today _____

(Omega-3 Fatty Acid is best for Your Brain Power and keeping your brain healthy.)
Great Sources of Omega-3s: *Salmon, Oysters, Caviar, Flax Seeds, Chia Seeds, and Walnuts.*
Other Great Sources of Brain Power – *Vitamins: B1, B6, B12, C, E, Antioxidants, Beta Carotene and Probiotics.*

Reminder: Cinnamon and Rosemary are great for neurological benefits.

Daily Exercise:

*If you are at the Beginning of your brain injury recovery, 5 minutes is great on the recumbent bike. OR if you are further along in recovery, a walk, weight bearing exercise and yoga are great choices. Remember not too much. Start slow and build up to 20 minutes. *Consult with your Dr for your proper exercise prescription.*

Exercise Log:
_____
_____
_____
_____
_____

Did you get your Yoga stillness today? ☐ yes ☐ no

This is your gateway to mental clarity and spiritual calm. Based on a centuries-old and scientifically proven pathway to health, Yoga is a gold star to your success. Great resources: Glo.com and Asanarebel.com

Daily Reflection:

Date: _____

I am grateful for ...

☼ _____
☼ _____
☼ _____

Positive Affirmations

☼ _____
☼ _____
☼ _____

Did you meditate?   ☐ yes   ☐ no

(At least 5 minutes, a great meditation APP: Calm.com)

Did you do the following?

Physical Therapy   ☐ yes   ☐ no

Occupational Therapy   ☐ yes   ☐ no

Speech Therapy   ☐ yes   ☐ no

Music Therapy   ☐ yes   ☐ no

Equine Therapy   ☐ yes   ☐ no

Cognitive Behavior Therapy ☐ yes   ☐ no

How did you feel?

☐ awesome   ☐ okay   ☐ not so good

Did you get a breath of Fresh Air Today?

☐ yes   ☐ no

Did you get your healthy 7-9 hrs of sleep?

☐ yes   ☐ no

Naps:

☐ 1-2 hours   ☐ 2-4 hours   ☐ other

Listening to music

Listening to music you love will make your brain release more dopamine! The naturally occurring happy chemical. Make sure to listen to more of your favorite tunes!

Meals Today:

*Be sure to add
Functional Foods in your diet*

Breakfast
_____

_____

Snack
_____

_____

Lunch
_____

_____

Snack
_____

_____

Dinner
_____

_____

Snack
_____

_____

Did you Spice up your day with Turmeric?   ☐ yes   ☐ no
(Best for Neuroprotection)

Did you get your Rainbow Greens today?   ☐ yes   ☐ no
(Dark Leafy Green is best for Brain Health)

Did you get Nuts/Seeds today?   ☐ yes   ☐ no

Vitamins I took today _____

(Omega-3 Fatty Acid is best for Your Brain Power and keeping your brain healthy.)
Great Sources of Omega-3s: *Salmon, Oysters, Caviar, Flax Seeds, Chia Seeds, and Walnuts.*
Other Great Sources of Brain Power *- Vitamins: B1, B6, B12, C, E, Antioxidants, Beta Carotene and Probiotics.*

Reminder: Cinnamon and Rosemary are great for neurological benefits.

Daily Exercise:

*If you are at the Beginning of your brain injury recovery, 5 minutes is great on the recumbent bike. OR if you are further along in recovery, a walk, weight bearing exercise and yoga are great choices. Remember not too much. Start slow and build up to 20 minutes. *Consult with your Dr for your proper exercise prescription.*

Exercise Log:
_____
_____
_____
_____

Did you get your Yoga stillness today?   ☐ yes   ☐ no

This is your gateway to mental clarity and spiritual calm. Based on a centuries-old and scientifically proven pathway to health, Yoga is a gold star to your success. Great resources: Glo.com and Asanarebel.com

Daily Reflection:

Date: _____

*Courage doesn't always roar. Sometimes courage is that
quiet voice at the end of the day saying,
I will try again tomorrow.*
- TBIhopeandinspiration.com

I am grateful for ...

☼ _____

☼ _____

☼ _____

Positive Affirmations

☼ _____

☼ _____

☼ _____

Did you meditate?   ☐ yes   ☐ no
(At least 5 minutes, a great meditation APP: Calm.com)

Did you do the following?

Physical Therapy   ☐ yes   ☐ no

Occupational Therapy   ☐ yes   ☐ no

Speech Therapy   ☐ yes   ☐ no

Music Therapy   ☐ yes   ☐ no

Equine Therapy   ☐ yes   ☐ no

Cognitive Behavior Therapy ☐ yes   ☐ no

How did you feel?

☐ *awesome*   ☐ *okay*   ☐ *not so good*

Did you get a breath of Fresh Air Today?

☐ *yes*   ☐ *no*

Did you get your healthy 7-9 hrs of sleep?

☐ *yes*   ☐ *no*

Naps:

☐ *1-2 hours*   ☐ *2-4 hours*   ☐ *other*

Listening to music

*Listening to music you love will make your
brain release more dopamine! The
naturally occurring happy chemical.
Make sure to listen to more of your favorite
tunes!*

Meals Today:

*Be sure to add
Functional Foods in your diet*

Breakfast
_____

_____

Snack
_____

_____

Lunch
_____

_____

Snack
_____

_____

Dinner
_____

_____

Snack
_____

_____

Did you Spice up your day with Turmeric? ☐ yes ☐ no

(Best for Neuroprotection)

Did you get your Rainbow Greens today? ☐ yes ☐ no

(Dark Leafy Green is best for Brain Health)

Did you get Nuts/Seeds today? ☐ yes ☐ no

Vitamins I took today _____

(Omega-3 Fatty Acid is best for Your Brain Power and keeping your brain healthy.)
Great Sources of Omega-3s: *Salmon, Oysters, Caviar, Flax Seeds, Chia Seeds, and Walnuts.*
Other Great Sources of Brain Power *– Vitamins: B1, B6, B12, C, E, Antioxidants, Beta Carotene and Probiotics.*

Reminder: Cinnamon and Rosemary are great for neurological benefits.

Daily Exercise:

*If you are at the Beginning of your brain injury recovery, 5 minutes is great on the recumbent bike. OR if you are further along in recovery, a walk, weight bearing exercise and yoga are great choices. Remember not too much. Start slow and build up to 20 minutes. *Consult with your Dr for your proper exercise prescription.*

Exercise Log:

_____

_____

_____

_____

Did you get your Yoga stillness today? ☐ yes ☐ no

This is your gateway to mental clarity and spiritual calm. Based on a centuries-old and scientifically proven pathway to health, Yoga is a gold star to your success. Great resources: Glo.com and Asanarebel.com

Daily Reflection:

Date: _____

I am not what has happened to me.
I am what I choose to become.
– Carl Jung

I am grateful for ...

☀ _____
☀ _____
☀ _____

Positive Affirmations

☀ _____
☀ _____
☀ _____

Did you meditate? ☐ yes ☐ no
(At least 5 minutes, a great meditation APP: Calm.com)

Did you do the following?

Physical Therapy ☐ yes ☐ no

Occupational Therapy ☐ yes ☐ no

Speech Therapy ☐ yes ☐ no

Music Therapy ☐ yes ☐ no

Equine Therapy ☐ yes ☐ no

Cognitive Behavior Therapy ☐ yes ☐ no

How did you feel?

☐ awesome ☐ okay ☐ not so good

Did you get a breath of Fresh Air Today?

☐ yes ☐ no

Did you get your healthy 7-9 hrs of sleep?

☐ yes ☐ no

Naps:

☐ 1-2 hours ☐ 2-4 hours ☐ other

Listening to music

Listening to music you love will make your brain release more dopamine! The naturally occurring happy chemical. Make sure to listen to more of your favorite tunes!

Meals Today:

Be sure to add
Functional Foods in your diet

Breakfast
_____
_____

Snack
_____
_____

Lunch
_____
_____

Snack
_____
_____

Dinner
_____
_____

Snack
_____
_____

Did you Spice up your day with Turmeric? ☐ yes ☐ no
(Best for Neuroprotection)

Did you get your Rainbow Greens today? ☐ yes ☐ no
(Dark Leafy Green is best for Brain Health)

Did you get Nuts/Seeds today? ☐ yes ☐ no

Vitamins I took today _____

(Omega-3 Fatty Acid is best for Your Brain Power and keeping your brain healthy.)
Great Sources of Omega-3s: *Salmon, Oysters, Caviar, Flax Seeds, Chia Seeds, and Walnuts.*
Other Great Sources of Brain Power - *Vitamins: B1, B6, B12, C, E, Antioxidants, Beta Carotene and Probiotics.*

Reminder: Cinnamon and Rosemary are great for neurological benefits.

Daily Exercise:

*If you are at the Beginning of your brain injury recovery, 5 minutes is great on the recumbent bike. OR if you are further along in recovery, a walk, weight bearing exercise and yoga are great choices. Remember not too much. Start slow and build up to 20 minutes. *Consult with your Dr for your proper exercise prescription.*

Exercise Log:
_____
_____
_____
_____

Did you get your Yoga stillness today? ☐ yes ☐ no

This is your gateway to mental clarity and spiritual calm. Based on a centuries-old and scientifically proven pathway to health, Yoga is a gold star to your success. Great resources: Glo.com and Asanarebel.com

Daily Reflection:

Date: _____

The whole world is a series of miracles, but we're so used to them we call them ordinary things.
– Hans Christian Anderson

I am grateful for ...

○ _____
○ _____
○ _____

Positive Affirmations

○ _____
○ _____
○ _____

Did you meditate? ☐ yes ☐ no

(At least 5 minutes, a great meditation APP: Calm.com)

Did you do the following?

Physical Therapy ☐ yes ☐ no

Occupational Therapy ☐ yes ☐ no

Speech Therapy ☐ yes ☐ no

Music Therapy ☐ yes ☐ no

Equine Therapy ☐ yes ☐ no

Cognitive Behavior Therapy ☐ yes ☐ no

How did you feel?

☐ awesome ☐ okay ☐ not so good

Did you get a breath of Fresh Air Today?

☐ yes ☐ no

Did you get your healthy 7-9 hrs of sleep?

☐ yes ☐ no

Naps:

☐ 1-2 hours ☐ 2-4 hours ☐ other

Listening to music

Listening to music you love will make your brain release more dopamine! The naturally occurring happy chemical. Make sure to listen to more of your favorite tunes!

Meals Today:

Be sure to add
Functional Foods in your diet

Breakfast
_____
_____

Snack
_____
_____

Lunch
_____
_____

Snack
_____
_____

Dinner
_____
_____

Snack
_____
_____

Did you Spice up your day with Turmeric? ☐ yes   ☐ no
(Best for Neuroprotection)

Did you get your Rainbow Greens today? ☐ yes   ☐ no
(Dark Leafy Green is best for Brain Health)

Did you get Nuts/Seeds today? ☐ yes   ☐ no

Vitamins I took today _____

(Omega-3 Fatty Acid is best for Your Brain Power and keeping your brain healthy.)
Great Sources of Omega-3s: *Salmon, Oysters, Caviar, Flax Seeds, Chia Seeds, and Walnuts.*
Other Great Sources of Brain Power *- Vitamins: B1, B6, B12, C, E, Antioxidants, Beta Carotene and Probiotics.*

Reminder: Cinnamon and Rosemary are great for neurological benefits.

Daily Exercise:

If you are at the Beginning of your brain injury recovery, 5 minutes is great on the recumbent bike. OR if you are further along in recovery, a walk, weight bearing exercise and yoga are great choices. Remember not too much. Start slow and build up to 20 minutes. *Consult with your Dr for your proper exercise prescription.

Exercise Log:

_____

_____

_____

_____

Did you get your Yoga stillness today? ☐ yes   ☐ no

This is your gateway to mental clarity and spiritual calm. Based on a centuries-old and scientifically proven pathway to health, Yoga is a gold star to your success. Great resources: Glo.com and Asanarebel.com

Daily Reflection:

Date: _____

I put one foot in front of the other...
I found one word and then I find another.
– Gabby Giffords

I am grateful for ...

☼ _____
☼ _____
☼ _____

Positive Affirmations

☼ _____
☼ _____
☼ _____

Did you meditate?　☐ yes　☐ no
(At least 5 minutes, a great meditation APP: Calm.com)

Did you do the following?

Physical Therapy　　　　☐ yes　☐ no

Occupational Therapy　　☐ yes　☐ no

Speech Therapy　　　　　☐ yes　☐ no

Music Therapy　　　　　☐ yes　☐ no

Equine Therapy　　　　　☐ yes　☐ no

Cognitive Behavior Therapy ☐ yes　☐ no

How did you feel?

☐ awesome　☐ okay　☐ not so good

Did you get a breath of Fresh Air Today?

☐ yes　　☐ no

Did you get your healthy 7-9 hrs of sleep?

☐ yes　　☐ no

Naps:

☐ 1-2 hours　☐ 2-4 hours　☐ other

Listening to music

Listening to music you love will make your brain release more dopamine! The naturally occurring happy chemical. Make sure to listen to more of your favorite tunes!

Meals Today:

Be sure to add
Functional Foods in your diet

Breakfast
_____

_____

Snack
_____

_____

Lunch
_____

_____

Snack
_____

_____

Dinner
_____

_____

Snack
_____

_____

Did you Spice up your day with Turmeric?   ☐ yes   ☐ no

(Best for Neuroprotection)

Did you get your Rainbow Greens today?   ☐ yes   ☐ no

(Dark Leafy Green is best for Brain Health)

Did you get Nuts/Seeds today?   ☐ yes   ☐ no

Vitamins I took today _____

(Omega-3 Fatty Acid is best for Your Brain Power and keeping your brain healthy.)
Great Sources of Omega-3s: *Salmon, Oysters, Caviar, Flax Seeds, Chia Seeds, and Walnuts.*
Other Great Sources of Brain Power – *Vitamins: B1, B6, B12, C, E, Antioxidants, Beta Carotene and Probiotics.*

Reminder: Cinnamon and Rosemary are great for neurological benefits.

Daily Exercise:

If you are at the Beginning of your brain injury recovery, 5 minutes is great on the recumbent bike. OR if you are further along in recovery, a walk, weight bearing exercise and yoga are great choices. Remember not too much. Start slow and build up to 20 minutes. *Consult with your Dr for your proper exercise prescription.

Exercise Log:
_____
_____
_____
_____

Did you get your Yoga stillness today?   ☐ yes   ☐ no

This is your gateway to mental clarity and spiritual calm. Based on a centuries-old and scientifically proven pathway to health, Yoga is a gold star to your success. Great resources: Glo.com and Asanarebel.com

Daily Reflection:

Date: _____

I love Someone with a Traumatic Brain Injury.
March is Brain Injury Awareness Month.

99

I am grateful for ...

☼ _____

☼ _____

☼ _____

Positive Affirmations

☼ _____

☼ _____

☼ _____

Did you meditate?   ☐ yes   ☐ no
(At least 5 minutes, a great meditation APP: Calm.com)

Did you do the following?

Physical Therapy   ☐ yes   ☐ no

Occupational Therapy   ☐ yes   ☐ no

Speech Therapy   ☐ yes   ☐ no

Music Therapy   ☐ yes   ☐ no

Equine Therapy   ☐ yes   ☐ no

Cognitive Behavior Therapy ☐ yes ☐ no

How did you feel?

☐ awesome   ☐ okay   ☐ not so good

Did you get a breath of Fresh Air Today?

☐ yes   ☐ no

Did you get your healthy 7-9 hrs of sleep?

☐ yes   ☐ no

Naps:

☐ 1-2 hours ☐ 2-4 hours ☐ other

Listening to music

Listening to music you love will make your brain release more dopamine! The naturally occurring happy chemical. Make sure to listen to more of your favorite tunes!

♪

Meals Today:

Be sure to add
Functional Foods in your diet

Breakfast _____

_____

Snack _____

_____

Lunch _____

_____

Snack _____

_____

Dinner _____

_____

Snack _____

_____

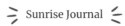

Did you Spice up your day with Turmeric?　　　☐ yes　☐ no

(Best for Neuroprotection)

Did you get your Rainbow Greens today?　　　☐ yes　☐ no

(Dark Leafy Green is best for Brain Health)

Did you get Nuts/Seeds today?　　　☐ yes　☐ no

Vitamins I took today _____

(Omega-3 Fatty Acid is best for Your Brain Power and keeping your brain healthy.)
Great Sources of Omega-3s: *Salmon, Oysters, Caviar, Flax Seeds, Chia Seeds, and Walnuts.*
Other Great Sources of Brain Power *– Vitamins: B1, B6, B12, C, E, Antioxidants, Beta Carotene and Probiotics.*

Reminder: Cinnamon and Rosemary are great for neurological benefits.

Daily Exercise:

If you are at the Beginning of your brain injury recovery, 5 minutes is great on the recumbent bike. OR if you are further along in recovery, a walk, weight bearing exercise and yoga are great choices. Remember not too much. Start slow and build up to 20 minutes. *Consult with your Dr for your proper exercise prescription.

Exercise Log:

_____

_____

_____

_____

Did you get your Yoga stillness today?　　　☐ yes　☐ no

This is your gateway to mental clarity and spiritual calm. Based on a centuries-old and scientifically proven pathway to health, Yoga is a gold star to your success. Great resources: Glo.com and Asanarebel.com

Daily Reflection:

Date: _____

I am grateful for …

 _____

_____

_____

Positive Affirmations

_____

_____

_____

Did you meditate? ☐ yes ☐ no

(At least 5 minutes, a great meditation APP: Calm.com)

Did you do the following?

Physical Therapy ☐ yes ☐ no

Occupational Therapy ☐ yes ☐ no

Speech Therapy ☐ yes ☐ no

Music Therapy ☐ yes ☐ no

Equine Therapy ☐ yes ☐ no

Cognitive Behavior Therapy ☐ yes ☐ no

How did you feel?

☐ awesome ☐ okay ☐ not so good

Did you get a breath of Fresh Air Today?

☐ yes ☐ no

Did you get your healthy 7-9 hrs of sleep?

☐ yes ☐ no

Naps:

☐ 1-2 hours ☐ 2-4 hours ☐ other

Listening to music

Listening to music you love will make your brain release more dopamine! The naturally occurring happy chemical. Make sure to listen to more of your favorite tunes!

Meals Today:

Be sure to add Functional Foods in your diet

Breakfast _____

_____

Snack _____

_____

Lunch _____

_____

Snack _____

_____

Dinner _____

_____

Snack _____

_____

Did you Spice up your day with Turmeric?   ☐ yes   ☐ no
(Best for Neuroprotection)

Did you get your Rainbow Greens today?   ☐ yes   ☐ no
(Dark Leafy Green is best for Brain Health)

Did you get Nuts/Seeds today?   ☐ yes   ☐ no

Vitamins I took today _____

(Omega-3 Fatty Acid is best for Your Brain Power and keeping your brain healthy.)
Great Sources of Omega-3s: *Salmon, Oysters, Caviar, Flax Seeds, Chia Seeds, and Walnuts.*
Other Great Sources of Brain Power - *Vitamins: B1, B6, B12, C, E, Antioxidants, Beta Carotene and Probiotics.*

> *Reminder: Cinnamon and Rosemary are great for neurological benefits.*

Daily Exercise:

If you are at the Beginning of your brain injury recovery, 5 minutes is great on the recumbent bike. OR if you are further along in recovery, a walk, weight bearing exercise and yoga are great choices. Remember not too much. Start slow and build up to 20 minutes. *Consult with your Dr for your proper exercise prescription.

Exercise Log:

Did you get your Yoga stillness today?   ☐ yes   ☐ no

This is your gateway to mental clarity and spiritual calm. Based on a centuries-old and scientifically proven pathway to health, Yoga is a gold star to your success. Great resources: Glo.com and Asanarebel.com

Daily Reflection:

Date: _____

Yes! Yes! You can do it!
– Unknown

I am grateful for ...

○ _____

○ _____

○ _____

Positive Affirmations

○ _____

○ _____

○ _____

Did you meditate?   ☐ yes   ☐ no
(At least 5 minutes, a great meditation APP: Calm.com)

Did you do the following?

Physical Therapy   ☐ yes   ☐ no

Occupational Therapy   ☐ yes   ☐ no

Speech Therapy   ☐ yes   ☐ no

Music Therapy   ☐ yes   ☐ no

Equine Therapy   ☐ yes   ☐ no

Cognitive Behavior Therapy ☐ yes   ☐ no

How did you feel?

☐ awesome   ☐ okay   ☐ not so good

Did you get a breath of Fresh Air Today?

☐ yes   ☐ no

Did you get your healthy 7-9 hrs of sleep?

☐ yes   ☐ no

Naps:

☐ 1-2 hours   ☐ 2-4 hours   ☐ other

Listening to music

Listening to music you love will make your brain release more dopamine! The naturally occurring happy chemical. Make sure to listen to more of your favorite tunes!

Meals Today:

Be sure to add
Functional Foods in your diet

Breakfast _____

_____

Snack _____

_____

Lunch _____

_____

Snack _____

_____

Dinner _____

_____

Snack _____

_____

Did you Spice up your day with Turmeric?　☐ yes　☐ no

(Best for Neuroprotection)

Did you get your Rainbow Greens today?　☐ yes　☐ no

(Dark Leafy Green is best for Brain Health)

Did you get Nuts/Seeds today?　☐ yes　☐ no

Vitamins I took today　_____

(Omega-3 Fatty Acid is best for Your Brain Power and keeping your brain healthy.)
Great Sources of Omega-3s: *Salmon, Oysters, Caviar, Flax Seeds, Chia Seeds, and Walnuts.*
Other Great Sources of Brain Power *- Vitamins: B1, B6, B12, C, E, Antioxidants, Beta Carotene and Probiotics.*

Reminder: Cinnamon and Rosemary are great for neurological benefits.

Daily Exercise:

*If you are at the Beginning of your brain injury recovery, 5 minutes is great on the recumbent bike. OR if you are further along in recovery, a walk, weight bearing exercise and yoga are great choices. Remember not too much. Start slow and build up to 20 minutes. *Consult with your Dr for your proper exercise prescription.*

Exercise Log:

_____

_____

_____

_____

_____

Did you get your Yoga stillness today?　☐ yes　☐ no

This is your gateway to mental clarity and spiritual calm. Based on a centuries-old and scientifically proven pathway to health, Yoga is a gold star to your success. Great resources: Glo.com and Asanarebel.com

Daily Reflection:

Date: _____

Tough times don't last;
Tough people do.
−Robert H. Schuller

I am grateful for ...

☀ _____

☀ _____

☀ _____

Did you meditate? ☐ yes ☐ no

(At least 5 minutes, a great meditation APP: Calm.com)

Did you do the following?

Physical Therapy ☐ yes ☐ no

Occupational Therapy ☐ yes ☐ no

Speech Therapy ☐ yes ☐ no

Music Therapy ☐ yes ☐ no

Equine Therapy ☐ yes ☐ no

Cognitive Behavior Therapy ☐ yes ☐ no

How did you feel?

☐ awesome ☐ okay ☐ not so good

Did you get a breath of Fresh Air Today?

☐ yes ☐ no

Did you get your healthy 7−9 hrs of sleep?

☐ yes ☐ no

Naps:

☐ 1-2 hours ☐ 2-4 hours ☐ other

Positive Affirmations

☀ _____

☀ _____

☀ _____

Listening to music

Listening to music you love will make your brain release more dopamine! The naturally occurring happy chemical. Make sure to listen to more of your favorite tunes!

Meals Today:

Be sure to add
Functional Foods in your diet

Breakfast
_____

_____

Snack
_____

_____

Lunch
_____

_____

Snack
_____

_____

Dinner
_____

_____

Snack
_____

_____

Did you Spice up your day with Turmeric? ☐ yes ☐ no
(Best for Neuroprotection)

Did you get your Rainbow Greens today? ☐ yes ☐ no
(Dark Leafy Green is best for Brain Health)

Did you get Nuts/Seeds today? ☐ yes ☐ no

Vitamins I took today _____

(Omega-3 Fatty Acid is best for Your Brain Power and keeping your brain healthy.)
Great Sources of Omega-3s: *Salmon, Oysters, Caviar, Flax Seeds, Chia Seeds, and Walnuts.*
Other Great Sources of Brain Power - *Vitamins: B1, B6, B12, C, E, Antioxidants, Beta Carotene and Probiotics.*

Reminder: Cinnamon and Rosemary are great for neurological benefits.

Daily Exercise:

If you are at the Beginning of your brain injury recovery, 5 minutes is great on the recumbent bike. OR if you are further along in recovery, a walk, weight bearing exercise and yoga are great choices. Remember not too much. Start slow and build up to 20 minutes. *Consult with your Dr for your proper exercise prescription.

Exercise Log:
_____
_____
_____
_____

Did you get your Yoga stillness today? ☐ yes ☐ no

This is your gateway to mental clarity and spiritual calm. Based on a centuries-old and scientifically proven pathway to health, Yoga is a gold star to your success. Great resources: Glo.com and Asanarebel.com

Daily Reflection:

Date: _____

Once you choose hope,
anything is possible.
–Christopher Reeve

I am grateful for ...

○ _____
○ _____
○ _____

Positive Affirmations

○ _____
○ _____
○ _____

Did you meditate?   ☐ yes   ☐ no
(At least 5 minutes, a great meditation APP: Calm.com)

Did you do the following?

Physical Therapy   ☐ yes   ☐ no
Occupational Therapy   ☐ yes   ☐ no
Speech Therapy   ☐ yes   ☐ no
Music Therapy   ☐ yes   ☐ no
Equine Therapy   ☐ yes   ☐ no
Cognitive Behavior Therapy ☐ yes   ☐ no

How did you feel?

☐ *awesome*   ☐ *okay*   ☐ *not so good*

Did you get a breath of Fresh Air Today?

☐ *yes*   ☐ *no*

Did you get your healthy 7-9 hrs of sleep?

☐ *yes*   ☐ *no*

Naps:

☐ *1-2 hours*   ☐ *2-4 hours*   ☐ *other*

Listening to music

Listening to music you love will make your brain release more dopamine! The naturally occurring happy chemical. Make sure to listen to more of your favorite tunes!

Meals Today:

Be sure to add
Functional Foods in your diet

Breakfast
_____
_____

Snack
_____
_____

Lunch
_____
_____

Snack
_____
_____

Dinner
_____
_____

Snack
_____
_____

Did you Spice up your day with Turmeric?   ☐ yes   ☐ no
(Best for Neuroprotection)

Did you get your Rainbow Greens today?   ☐ yes   ☐ no
(Dark Leafy Green is best for Brain Health)

Did you get Nuts/Seeds today?   ☐ yes   ☐ no

Vitamins I took today _____

(Omega-3 Fatty Acid is best for Your Brain Power and keeping your brain healthy.)
Great Sources of Omega-3s: *Salmon, Oysters, Caviar, Flax Seeds, Chia Seeds, and Walnuts.*
Other Great Sources of Brain Power - *Vitamins: B1, B6, B12, C, E, Antioxidants, Beta Carotene and Probiotics.*

Reminder: Cinnamon and Rosemary are great for neurological benefits.

Daily Exercise:

*If you are at the Beginning of your brain injury recovery, 5 minutes is great on the recumbent bike. OR if you are further along in recovery, a walk, weight bearing exercise and yoga are great choices. Remember not too much. Start slow and build up to 20 minutes. *Consult with your Dr for your proper exercise prescription.*

Exercise Log:
_____
_____
_____
_____

Did you get your Yoga stillness today?   ☐ yes   ☐ no

This is your gateway to mental clarity and spiritual calm. Based on a centuries-old and scientifically proven pathway to health, Yoga is a gold star to your success. Great resources: Glo.com and Asanarebel.com

Daily Reflection:

Date: _____

That's the good part about injury, it
strengthens you in many ways.
– Bojan Krkic

I am grateful for ...

Positive Affirmations

☼ _____

☼ _____

☼ _____

☼ _____

☼ _____

☼ _____

Did you meditate?　□ yes　□ no
(At least 5 minutes, a great meditation APP: Calm.com)

Did you do the following?

Physical Therapy　□ yes　□ no

Occupational Therapy　□ yes　□ no

Speech Therapy　□ yes　□ no

Music Therapy　□ yes　□ no

Equine Therapy　□ yes　□ no

Cognitive Behavior Therapy □ yes　□ no

How did you feel?

□ awesome　□ okay　□ not so good

Did you get a breath of Fresh Air Today?

□ yes　　□ no

Did you get your healthy 7-9 hrs of sleep?

□ yes　　□ no

Naps:

□ *1-2 hours*　□ *2-4 hours*　□ *other*

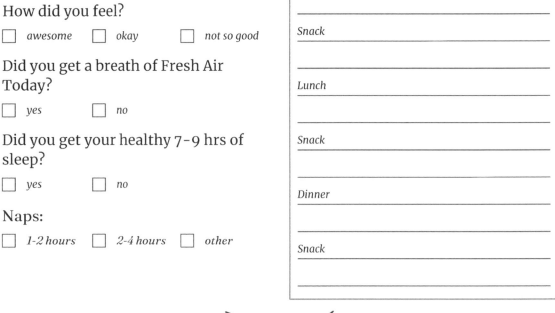

Listening to music

Listening to music you love will make your brain release more dopamine! The naturally occurring happy chemical. Make sure to listen to more of your favorite tunes!

Meals Today:

Be sure to add
Functional Foods in your diet

Breakfast
_____

_____

Snack
_____

_____

Lunch
_____

_____

Snack
_____

_____

Dinner
_____

_____

Snack
_____

_____

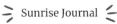

Did you Spice up your day with Turmeric? ☐ yes ☐ no
(Best for Neuroprotection)

Did you get your Rainbow Greens today? ☐ yes ☐ no
(Dark Leafy Green is best for Brain Health)

Did you get Nuts/Seeds today? ☐ yes ☐ no

Vitamins I took today _____

(Omega-3 Fatty Acid is best for Your Brain Power and keeping your brain healthy.)
Great Sources of Omega-3s: *Salmon, Oysters, Caviar, Flax Seeds, Chia Seeds, and Walnuts.*
Other Great Sources of Brain Power - *Vitamins: B1, B6, B12, C, E, Antioxidants, Beta Carotene and Probiotics.*

Reminder: Cinnamon and Rosemary are great for neurological benefits.

Daily Exercise:

*If you are at the Beginning of your brain injury recovery, 5 minutes is great on the recumbent bike. OR if you are further along in recovery, a walk, weight bearing exercise and yoga are great choices. Remember not too much. Start slow and build up to 20 minutes. *Consult with your Dr for your proper exercise prescription.*

Exercise Log:
_____
_____
_____
_____

Did you get your Yoga stillness today? ☐ yes ☐ no

This is your gateway to mental clarity and spiritual calm. Based on a centuries-old and scientifically proven pathway to health, Yoga is a gold star to your success. Great resources: Glo.com and Asanarebel.com

Daily Reflection:

Date: _____

Laughter is timeless.
Imagination has no age.
And dreams are forever.
– Walt Disney

I am grateful for ...

○ _____

○ _____

○ _____

Positive Affirmations

○ _____

○ _____

○ _____

Did you meditate? ☐ yes ☐ no
(At least 5 minutes, a great meditation APP: Calm.com)

Did you do the following?

Physical Therapy ☐ yes ☐ no

Occupational Therapy ☐ yes ☐ no

Speech Therapy ☐ yes ☐ no

Music Therapy ☐ yes ☐ no

Equine Therapy ☐ yes ☐ no

Cognitive Behavior Therapy ☐ yes ☐ no

How did you feel?

☐ awesome ☐ okay ☐ not so good

Did you get a breath of Fresh Air Today?

☐ yes ☐ no

Did you get your healthy 7-9 hrs of sleep?

☐ yes ☐ no

Naps:

☐ 1-2 hours ☐ 2-4 hours ☐ other

Listening to music

Listening to music you love will make your brain release more dopamine! The naturally occurring happy chemical. Make sure to listen to more of your favorite tunes!

Meals Today:

Be sure to add
Functional Foods in your diet

Breakfast
_____

_____

Snack
_____

_____

Lunch
_____

_____

Snack
_____

_____

Dinner
_____

_____

Snack
_____

_____

Did you Spice up your day with Turmeric?　　　☐ *yes*　☐ *no*
(Best for Neuroprotection)

Did you get your Rainbow Greens today?　　　☐ *yes*　☐ *no*
(Dark Leafy Green is best for Brain Health)

Did you get Nuts/Seeds today?　　　　　　　☐ *yes*　☐ *no*

Vitamins I took today _____

(Omega-3 Fatty Acid is best for Your Brain Power and keeping your brain healthy.)
Great Sources of Omega-3s: *Salmon, Oysters, Caviar, Flax Seeds, Chia Seeds, and Walnuts.*
Other Great Sources of Brain Power *- Vitamins: B1, B6, B12, C, E, Antioxidants, Beta Carotene and Probiotics.*

Reminder: Cinnamon and Rosemary are great for neurological benefits.

Daily Exercise:

*If you are at the Beginning of your brain injury recovery, 5 minutes is great on the recumbent bike. OR if you are further along in recovery, a walk, weight bearing exercise and yoga are great choices. Remember not too much. Start slow and build up to 20 minutes. *Consult with your Dr for your proper exercise prescription.*

Exercise Log:
_____
_____
_____
_____

Did you get your Yoga stillness today?　　　☐ *yes*　☐ *no*

This is your gateway to mental clarity and spiritual calm. Based on a centuries-old and scientifically proven pathway to health, Yoga is a gold star to your success. Great resources: Glo.com and Asanarebel.com

Daily Reflection:

Date: _____

I am grateful for ...

☼ _____

☼ _____

☼ _____

Positive Affirmations

☼ _____

☼ _____

☼ _____

Did you meditate? ☐ yes ☐ no
(At least 5 minutes, a great meditation APP: Calm.com)

Did you do the following?

Physical Therapy ☐ yes ☐ no

Occupational Therapy ☐ yes ☐ no

Speech Therapy ☐ yes ☐ no

Music Therapy ☐ yes ☐ no

Equine Therapy ☐ yes ☐ no

Cognitive Behavior Therapy ☐ yes ☐ no

How did you feel?

☐ *awesome* ☐ *okay* ☐ *not so good*

Did you get a breath of Fresh Air Today?

☐ *yes* ☐ *no*

Did you get your healthy 7-9 hrs of sleep?

☐ *yes* ☐ *no*

Naps:

☐ *1-2 hours* ☐ *2-4 hours* ☐ *other*

Listening to music

Listening to music you love will make your brain release more dopamine! The naturally occurring happy chemical. Make sure to listen to more of your favorite tunes!

Meals Today:

Be sure to add
Functional Foods in your diet

Breakfast
_____
_____

Snack
_____
_____

Lunch
_____
_____

Snack
_____
_____

Dinner
_____
_____

Snack
_____
_____

Did you Spice up your day with Turmeric?　　　☐ yes　☐ no

(Best for Neuroprotection)

Did you get your Rainbow Greens today?　　　☐ yes　☐ no

(Dark Leafy Green is best for Brain Health)

Did you get Nuts/Seeds today?　　　☐ yes　☐ no

Vitamins I took today　_____

(Omega-3 Fatty Acid is best for Your Brain Power and keeping your brain healthy.)
Great Sources of Omega-3s: *Salmon, Oysters, Caviar, Flax Seeds, Chia Seeds, and Walnuts.*
Other Great Sources of Brain Power – *Vitamins: B1, B6, B12, C, E, Antioxidants, Beta Carotene and Probiotics.*

Reminder: Cinnamon and Rosemary are great for neurological benefits.

Daily Exercise:

*If you are at the Beginning of your brain injury recovery, 5 minutes is great on the recumbent bike. OR if you are further along in recovery, a walk, weight bearing exercise and yoga are great choices. Remember not too much. Start slow and build up to 20 minutes. *Consult with your Dr for your proper exercise prescription.*

Exercise Log:

_____
_____
_____
_____
_____

Did you get your Yoga stillness today?　　　☐ yes　☐ no

This is your gateway to mental clarity and spiritual calm. Based on a centuries-old and scientifically proven pathway to health, Yoga is a gold star to your success. Great resources: Glo.com and Asanarebel.com

Daily Reflection:

Date: _____

Some quit to slow progress.
Never grasping the fact that slow progress...
...is progress.
−Jeff Olson

I am grateful for ...

☼ _____
☼ _____
☼ _____

Positive Affirmations

☼ _____
☼ _____
☼ _____

Did you meditate? ☐ yes ☐ no

(At least 5 minutes, a great meditation APP: Calm.com)

Did you do the following?

Physical Therapy ☐ yes ☐ no

Occupational Therapy ☐ yes ☐ no

Speech Therapy ☐ yes ☐ no

Music Therapy ☐ yes ☐ no

Equine Therapy ☐ yes ☐ no

Cognitive Behavior Therapy ☐ yes ☐ no

How did you feel?

☐ awesome ☐ okay ☐ not so good

Did you get a breath of Fresh Air Today?

☐ yes ☐ no

Did you get your healthy 7-9 hrs of sleep?

☐ yes ☐ no

Naps:

☐ 1-2 hours ☐ 2-4 hours ☐ other

Listening to music

Listening to music you love will make your brain release more dopamine! The naturally occurring happy chemical. Make sure to listen to more of your favorite tunes!

Meals Today:

Be sure to add
Functional Foods in your diet

Breakfast
_____
_____

Snack
_____
_____

Lunch
_____
_____

Snack
_____
_____

Dinner
_____
_____

Snack
_____
_____

Did you Spice up your day with Turmeric?   ☐ yes   ☐ no

(Best for Neuroprotection)

Did you get your Rainbow Greens today?   ☐ yes   ☐ no

(Dark Leafy Green is best for Brain Health)

Did you get Nuts/Seeds today?   ☐ yes   ☐ no

Vitamins I took today _____

(Omega-3 Fatty Acid is best for Your Brain Power and keeping your brain healthy.)
Great Sources of Omega-3s: *Salmon, Oysters, Caviar, Flax Seeds, Chia Seeds, and Walnuts.*
Other Great Sources of Brain Power *- Vitamins: B1, B6, B12, C, E, Antioxidants, Beta Carotene and Probiotics.*

Reminder: Cinnamon and Rosemary are great for neurological benefits.

Daily Exercise:

*If you are at the Beginning of your brain injury recovery, 5 minutes is great on the recumbent bike. OR if you are further along in recovery, a walk, weight bearing exercise and yoga are great choices. Remember not too much. Start slow and build up to 20 minutes. *Consult with your Dr for your proper exercise prescription.*

Exercise Log:

_____

_____

_____

_____

Did you get your Yoga stillness today?   ☐ yes   ☐ no

This is your gateway to mental clarity and spiritual calm. Based on a centuries-old and scientifically proven pathway to health, Yoga is a gold star to your success. Great resources: Glo.com and Asanarebel.com

Daily Reflection:

Date: _____

*Never let a stumble in the road be the end
of the journey.
–Unknown*

I am grateful for ...

- ☼ _____
- ☼ _____
- ☼ _____

Positive Affirmations

- ☼ _____
- ☼ _____
- ☼ _____

Did you meditate?   ☐ yes   ☐ no
(At least 5 minutes, a great meditation APP: Calm.com)

Did you do the following?

Physical Therapy	☐ yes	☐ no
Occupational Therapy	☐ yes	☐ no
Speech Therapy	☐ yes	☐ no
Music Therapy	☐ yes	☐ no
Equine Therapy	☐ yes	☐ no
Cognitive Behavior Therapy	☐ yes	☐ no

How did you feel?

☐ *awesome*   ☐ *okay*   ☐ *not so good*

Did you get a breath of Fresh Air Today?

☐ *yes*   ☐ *no*

Did you get your healthy 7-9 hrs of sleep?

☐ *yes*   ☐ *no*

Naps:

☐ *1-2 hours*   ☐ *2-4 hours*   ☐ *other*

Listening to music

Listening to music you love will make your brain release more dopamine! The naturally occurring happy chemical. Make sure to listen to more of your favorite tunes!

Meals Today:

*Be sure to add
Functional Foods in your diet*

Breakfast
_____
_____

Snack
_____
_____

Lunch
_____
_____

Snack
_____
_____

Dinner
_____
_____

Snack
_____
_____

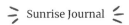

Did you Spice up your day with Turmeric? ☐ yes ☐ no
(Best for Neuroprotection)

Did you get your Rainbow Greens today? ☐ yes ☐ no
(Dark Leafy Green is best for Brain Health)

Did you get Nuts/Seeds today? ☐ yes ☐ no

Vitamins I took today _____

(Omega-3 Fatty Acid is best for Your Brain Power and keeping your brain healthy.)
Great Sources of Omega-3s: *Salmon, Oysters, Caviar, Flax Seeds, Chia Seeds, and Walnuts.*
Other Great Sources of Brain Power – *Vitamins: B1, B6, B12, C, E, Antioxidants, Beta Carotene and Probiotics.*

> *Reminder: Cinnamon and Rosemary are great for neurological benefits.*

Daily Exercise:

If you are at the Beginning of your brain injury recovery, 5 minutes is great on the recumbent bike. OR if you are further along in recovery, a walk, weight bearing exercise and yoga are great choices. Remember not too much. Start slow and build up to 20 minutes. *Consult with your Dr for your proper exercise prescription.

Exercise Log:
_____
_____
_____
_____
_____

Did you get your Yoga stillness today? ☐ yes ☐ no

This is your gateway to mental clarity and spiritual calm. Based on a centuries-old and scientifically proven pathway to health, Yoga is a gold star to your success. Great resources: Glo.com and Asanarebel.com

Daily Reflection:

Date: _____

*It does not matter how slowly you go as
long as you do not stop.*
– Confucius

I am grateful for ...

○ _____

○ _____

○ _____

Positive Affirmations

○ _____

○ _____

○ _____

Did you meditate? ☐ yes ☐ no

(At least 5 minutes, a great meditation APP: Calm.com)

Did you do the following?

Physical Therapy ☐ yes ☐ no

Occupational Therapy ☐ yes ☐ no

Speech Therapy ☐ yes ☐ no

Music Therapy ☐ yes ☐ no

Equine Therapy ☐ yes ☐ no

Cognitive Behavior Therapy ☐ yes ☐ no

How did you feel?

☐ awesome ☐ okay ☐ not so good

Did you get a breath of Fresh Air
Today?

☐ yes ☐ no

Did you get your healthy 7-9 hrs of
sleep?

☐ yes ☐ no

Naps:

☐ 1-2 hours ☐ 2-4 hours ☐ other

Listening to music

*Listening to music you love will make your
brain release more dopamine! The
naturally occurring happy chemical.
Make sure to listen to more of your favorite
tunes!*

Meals Today:

*Be sure to add
Functional Foods in your diet*

Breakfast
_____

_____

Snack
_____

_____

Lunch
_____

_____

Snack
_____

_____

Dinner
_____

_____

Snack
_____

_____

Did you Spice up your day with Turmeric? ☐ yes ☐ no
(Best for Neuroprotection)

Did you get your Rainbow Greens today? ☐ yes ☐ no
(Dark Leafy Green is best for Brain Health)

Did you get Nuts/Seeds today? ☐ yes ☐ no

Vitamins I took today _____

(Omega-3 Fatty Acid is best for Your Brain Power and keeping your brain healthy.)
Great Sources of Omega-3s: *Salmon, Oysters, Caviar, Flax Seeds, Chia Seeds, and Walnuts.*
Other Great Sources of Brain Power - *Vitamins: B1, B6, B12, C, E, Antioxidants, Beta Carotene and Probiotics.*

Reminder: Cinnamon and Rosemary are great for neurological benefits.

Daily Exercise:

*If you are at the Beginning of your brain injury recovery, 5 minutes is great on the recumbent bike. OR if you are further along in recovery, a walk, weight bearing exercise and yoga are great choices. Remember not too much. Start slow and build up to 20 minutes. *Consult with your Dr for your proper exercise prescription.*

Exercise Log:
_____
_____
_____
_____

Did you get your Yoga stillness today? ☐ yes ☐ no

This is your gateway to mental clarity and spiritual calm. Based on a centuries-old and scientifically proven pathway to health, Yoga is a gold star to your success. Great resources: Glo.com and Asanarebel.com

Daily Reflection:

Date: _____

Get better every single day.
–Unknown

I am grateful for ...

☼ _____

☼ _____

☼ _____

Positive Affirmations

☼ _____

☼ _____

☼ _____

Did you meditate? ☐ *yes* ☐ *no*
(At least 5 minutes, a great meditation APP: Calm.com)

Did you do the following?

Physical Therapy ☐ *yes* ☐ *no*

Occupational Therapy ☐ *yes* ☐ *no*

Speech Therapy ☐ *yes* ☐ *no*

Music Therapy ☐ *yes* ☐ *no*

Equine Therapy ☐ *yes* ☐ *no*

Cognitive Behavior Therapy ☐ *yes* ☐ *no*

How did you feel?

☐ *awesome* ☐ *okay* ☐ *not so good*

Did you get a breath of Fresh Air Today?

☐ *yes* ☐ *no*

Did you get your healthy 7-9 hrs of sleep?

☐ *yes* ☐ *no*

Naps:

☐ *1-2 hours* ☐ *2-4 hours* ☐ *other*

Listening to music

Listening to music you love will make your brain release more dopamine! The naturally occurring happy chemical. Make sure to listen to more of your favorite tunes!

Meals Today:

*Be sure to add
Functional Foods in your diet*

Breakfast
_____

Snack
_____

Lunch
_____

Snack
_____

Dinner
_____

Snack
_____

Did you Spice up your day with Turmeric?　　☐ yes　☐ no

(Best for Neuroprotection)

Did you get your Rainbow Greens today?　　☐ yes　☐ no

(Dark Leafy Green is best for Brain Health)

Did you get Nuts/Seeds today?　　☐ yes　☐ no

Vitamins I took today _____

(Omega-3 Fatty Acid is best for Your Brain Power and keeping your brain healthy.)
Great Sources of Omega-3s: *Salmon, Oysters, Caviar, Flax Seeds, Chia Seeds, and Walnuts.*
Other Great Sources of Brain Power *– Vitamins: B1, B6, B12, C, E, Antioxidants, Beta Carotene and Probiotics.*

> ### Reminder: Cinnamon and Rosemary are great for neurological benefits.

Daily Exercise:

*If you are at the Beginning of your brain injury recovery, 5 minutes is great on the recumbent bike. OR if you are further along in recovery, a walk, weight bearing exercise and yoga are great choices. Remember not too much. Start slow and build up to 20 minutes. *Consult with your Dr for your proper exercise prescription.*

Exercise Log:

_____

_____

_____

_____

Did you get your Yoga stillness today?　　☐ yes　☐ no

This is your gateway to mental clarity and spiritual calm. Based on a centuries-old and scientifically proven pathway to health, Yoga is a gold star to your success. Great resources: Glo.com and Asanarebel.com

Daily Reflection:

Date: _____

I am grateful for …

☀ _____

☀ _____

☀ _____

Positive Affirmations

☀ _____

☀ _____

☀ _____

Did you meditate?   ☐ yes   ☐ no
(At least 5 minutes, a great meditation APP: Calm.com)

Did you do the following?

Physical Therapy   ☐ yes   ☐ no

Occupational Therapy   ☐ yes   ☐ no

Speech Therapy   ☐ yes   ☐ no

Music Therapy   ☐ yes   ☐ no

Equine Therapy   ☐ yes   ☐ no

Cognitive Behavior Therapy ☐ yes   ☐ no

How did you feel?

☐ awesome   ☐ okay   ☐ not so good

Did you get a breath of Fresh Air Today?

☐ yes   ☐ no

Did you get your healthy 7-9 hrs of sleep?

☐ yes   ☐ no

Naps:

☐ 1-2 hours   ☐ 2-4 hours   ☐ other

Listening to music

Listening to music you love will make your brain release more dopamine! The naturally occurring happy chemical. Make sure to listen to more of your favorite tunes! ♫

Meals Today:

Be sure to add Functional Foods in your diet

Breakfast _____

_____

Snack _____

_____

Lunch _____

_____

Snack _____

_____

Dinner _____

_____

Snack _____

_____

Did you Spice up your day with Turmeric?　　　☐ yes　☐ no

(Best for Neuroprotection)

Did you get your Rainbow Greens today?　　　☐ yes　☐ no

(Dark Leafy Green is best for Brain Health)

Did you get Nuts/Seeds today?　　　☑ yes　☐ no

Vitamins I took today　　＿＿＿＿＿＿＿＿＿＿＿＿＿＿＿＿＿＿

(Omega-3 Fatty Acid is best for Your Brain Power and keeping your brain healthy.)
Great Sources of Omega-3s: *Salmon, Oysters, Caviar, Flax Seeds, Chia Seeds, and Walnuts.*
Other Great Sources of Brain Power – *Vitamins: B1, B6, B12, C, E, Antioxidants, Beta Carotene and Probiotics.*

Reminder: Cinnamon and Rosemary are great for neurological benefits.

Daily Exercise:

*If you are at the Beginning of your brain injury recovery, 5 minutes is great on the recumbent bike. OR if you are further along in recovery, a walk, weight bearing exercise and yoga are great choices. Remember not too much. Start slow and build up to 20 minutes. *Consult with your Dr for your proper exercise prescription.*

Exercise Log:
＿＿＿＿＿＿＿＿＿＿＿
＿＿＿＿＿＿＿＿＿＿＿
＿＿＿＿＿＿＿＿＿＿＿
＿＿＿＿＿＿＿＿＿＿＿

Did you get your Yoga stillness today?　　　☐ yes　☐ no

This is your gateway to mental clarity and spiritual calm. Based on a centuries-old and scientifically proven pathway to health, Yoga is a gold star to your success. Great resources: Glo.com and Asanarebel.com

Daily Reflection:

Date: _____

Learn from Greatness.

I am grateful for ...

○ _____
○ _____
○ _____

Positive Affirmations

○ _____
○ _____
○ _____

Did you meditate? ☐ yes ☐ no
(At least 5 minutes, a great meditation APP: Calm.com)

Did you do the following?

Physical Therapy ☐ yes ☐ no

Occupational Therapy ☐ yes ☐ no

Speech Therapy ☐ yes ☐ no

Music Therapy ☐ yes ☐ no

Equine Therapy ☐ yes ☐ no

Cognitive Behavior Therapy ☐ yes ☐ no

How did you feel?

☐ awesome ☐ okay ☐ not so good

Did you get a breath of Fresh Air Today?

☐ yes ☐ no

Did you get your healthy 7-9 hrs of sleep?

☐ yes ☐ no

Naps:

☐ 1-2 hours ☐ 2-4 hours ☐ other

Listening to music

Listening to music you love will make your brain release more dopamine! The naturally occurring happy chemical. Make sure to listen to more of your favorite tunes!

Meals Today:

Be sure to add Functional Foods in your diet

Breakfast _____
_____

Snack _____
_____

Lunch _____
_____

Snack _____
_____

Dinner _____
_____

Snack _____
_____

Did you Spice up your day with Turmeric?   ☐ yes   ☐ no
(Best for Neuroprotection)

Did you get your Rainbow Greens today?   ☐ yes   ☐ no
(Dark Leafy Green is best for Brain Health)

Did you get Nuts/Seeds today?   ☑ yes   ☐ no

Vitamins I took today _____

(Omega-3 Fatty Acid is best for Your Brain Power and keeping your brain healthy.)
Great Sources of Omega-3s: *Salmon, Oysters, Caviar, Flax Seeds, Chia Seeds, and Walnuts.*
Other Great Sources of Brain Power – *Vitamins: B1, B6, B12, C, E, Antioxidants, Beta Carotene and Probiotics.*

> *Reminder: Cinnamon and Rosemary are great for neurological benefits.*

Daily Exercise:

If you are at the Beginning of your brain injury recovery, 5 minutes is great on the recumbent bike. OR if you are further along in recovery, a walk, weight bearing exercise and yoga are great choices. Remember not too much. Start slow and build up to 20 minutes. *Consult with your Dr for your proper exercise prescription.

Exercise Log:
_____
_____
_____
_____
_____

Did you get your Yoga stillness today?   ☐ yes   ☐ no

This is your gateway to mental clarity and spiritual calm. Based on a centuries-old and scientifically proven pathway to health, Yoga is a gold star to your success. Great resources: Glo.com and Asanarebel.com

Daily Reflection:

Date: _____

Be Ambitious.

___ "

I am grateful for ...

☼ _____

☼ _____

☼ _____

Positive Affirmations

☼ _____

☼ _____

☼ _____

Did you meditate?　☐ *yes*　☐ *no*

(At least 5 minutes, a great meditation APP: Calm.com)

Did you do the following?

Physical Therapy　☐ *yes*　☐ *no*

Occupational Therapy　☐ *yes*　☐ *no*

Speech Therapy　☐ *yes*　☐ *no*

Music Therapy　☐ *yes*　☐ *no*

Equine Therapy　☐ *yes*　☐ *no*

Cognitive Behavior Therapy ☐ *yes*　☐ *no*

How did you feel?

☐ *awesome*　☐ *okay*　☐ *not so good*

Did you get a breath of Fresh Air Today?

☐ *yes*　☐ *no*

Did you get your healthy 7-9 hrs of sleep?

☐ *yes*　☐ *no*

Naps:

☐ *1-2 hours*　☐ *2-4 hours*　☐ *other*

Listening to music

Listening to music you love will make your brain release more dopamine! The naturally occurring happy chemical. Make sure to listen to more of your favorite tunes!

Meals Today:

Be sure to add Functional Foods in your diet

Breakfast
_____
_____

Snack
_____
_____

Lunch
_____
_____

Snack
_____
_____

Dinner
_____
_____

Snack
_____
_____

Did you Spice up your day with Turmeric? ☑ *yes* ☐ *no*

(Best for Neuroprotection)

Did you get your Rainbow Greens today? ☑ *yes* ☐ *no*

(Dark Leafy Green is best for Brain Health)

Did you get Nuts/Seeds today? ☑ *yes* ☐ *no*

Vitamins I took today _____

(Omega-3 Fatty Acid is best for Your Brain Power and keeping your brain healthy.)
Great Sources of Omega-3s: *Salmon, Oysters, Caviar, Flax Seeds, Chia Seeds, and Walnuts.*
Other Great Sources of Brain Power *- Vitamins: B1, B6, B12, C, E, Antioxidants, Beta Carotene and Probiotics.*

Reminder: Cinnamon and Rosemary are great for neurological benefits.

Daily Exercise:

*If you are at the Beginning of your brain injury recovery, 5 minutes is great on the recumbent bike. OR if you are further along in recovery, a walk, weight bearing exercise and yoga are great choices. Remember not too much. Start slow and build up to 20 minutes. *Consult with your Dr for your proper exercise prescription.*

Exercise Log:

_____

_____

_____

_____

Did you get your Yoga stillness today? ☐ *yes* ☐ *no*

This is your gateway to mental clarity and spiritual calm. Based on a centuries-old and scientifically proven pathway to health. Yoga is a gold star to your success. Great resources: Glo.com and Asanarebel.com

Daily Reflection:

Date: _____

*The most certain way to succeed is always to try
just one more time.*
- Thomas Edison

I am grateful for ...

○ _____
○ _____
○ _____

Positive Affirmations

○ _____
○ _____
○ _____

Did you meditate?   ☐ yes   ☐ no
(At least 5 minutes, a great meditation APP: Calm.com)

Did you do the following?

Physical Therapy	☐ yes	☐ no
Occupational Therapy	☐ yes	☐ no
Speech Therapy	☐ yes	☐ no
Music Therapy	☐ yes	☐ no
Equine Therapy	☐ yes	☐ no
Cognitive Behavior Therapy ☐ yes	☐ no

How did you feel?

☐ *awesome*   ☐ *okay*   ☐ *not so good*

Did you get a breath of Fresh Air Today?

☐ *yes*   ☐ *no*

Did you get your healthy 7-9 hrs of sleep?

☐ *yes*   ☐ *no*

Naps:

☐ *1-2 hours*   ☐ *2-4 hours*   ☐ *other*

Listening to music

Listening to music you love will make your brain release more dopamine! The naturally occurring happy chemical. Make sure to listen to more of your favorite tunes!

Meals Today:

*Be sure to add
Functional Foods in your diet*

Breakfast
_____

Snack
_____

Lunch
_____

Snack
_____

Dinner
_____

Snack
_____
_____

Did you Spice up your day with Turmeric?　☐ *yes*　☐ *no*

(Best for Neuroprotection)

Did you get your Rainbow Greens today?　☐ *yes*　☐ *no*

(Dark Leafy Green is best for Brain Health)

Did you get Nuts/Seeds today?　☐ *yes*　☐ *no*

Vitamins I took today _____

(Omega-3 Fatty Acid is best for Your Brain Power and keeping your brain healthy.)
Great Sources of Omega-3s: *Salmon, Oysters, Caviar, Flax Seeds, Chia Seeds, and Walnuts.*
Other Great Sources of Brain Power *- Vitamins: B1, B6, B12, C, E, Antioxidants, Beta Carotene and Probiotics.*

Reminder: Cinnamon and Rosemary are great for neurological benefits.

Daily Exercise:

*If you are at the Beginning of your brain injury recovery, 5 minutes is great on the recumbent bike. OR if you are further along in recovery, a walk, weight bearing exercise and yoga are great choices. Remember not too much. Start slow and build up to 20 minutes. *Consult with your Dr for your proper exercise prescription.*

Exercise Log:
_____
_____
_____
_____

Did you get your Yoga stillness today?　☐ *yes*　☐ *no*

This is your gateway to mental clarity and spiritual calm. Based on a centuries-old and scientifically proven pathway to health, Yoga is a gold star to your success. Great resources: Glo.com and Asanarebel.com

Daily Reflection:

Date: _____

Grit /grit/noun:
strength of character; perseverance and passion
for long-term goals.

I am grateful for ...

- ☼ _____
- ☼ _____
- ☼ _____

Positive Affirmations

- ☼ _____
- ☼ _____
- ☼ _____

Did you meditate?   ☐ yes   ☐ no
(At least 5 minutes, a great meditation APP: Calm.com)

Did you do the following?

Physical Therapy	☐ yes	☐ no
Occupational Therapy	☐ yes	☐ no
Speech Therapy	☐ yes	☐ no
Music Therapy	☐ yes	☐ no
Equine Therapy	☐ yes	☐ no
Cognitive Behavior Therapy	☐ yes	☐ no

How did you feel?

☐ *awesome*   ☐ *okay*   ☐ *not so good*

Did you get a breath of Fresh Air Today?

☐ *yes*   ☐ *no*

Did you get your healthy 7-9 hrs of sleep?

☐ *yes*   ☐ *no*

Naps:

☐ *1-2 hours*   ☐ *2-4 hours*   ☐ *other*

Listening to music

Listening to music you love will make your brain release more dopamine! The naturally occurring happy chemical. Make sure to listen to more of your favorite tunes!

♫

Meals Today:

Be sure to add
Functional Foods in your diet

Breakfast
_____
_____

Snack
_____

Lunch
_____

Snack
_____

Dinner
_____

Snack
_____
_____

Did you Spice up your day with Turmeric?　　☐ yes　☐ no

(Best for Neuroprotection)

Did you get your Rainbow Greens today?　　☐ yes　☐ no

(Dark Leafy Green is best for Brain Health)

Did you get Nuts/Seeds today?　　☐ yes　☐ no

Vitamins I took today _____

(Omega-3 Fatty Acid is best for Your Brain Power and keeping your brain healthy.)
Great Sources of Omega-3s: *Salmon, Oysters, Caviar, Flax Seeds, Chia Seeds, and Walnuts.*
Other Great Sources of Brain Power *- Vitamins: B1, B6, B12, C, E, Antioxidants, Beta Carotene and Probiotics.*

> *Reminder: Cinnamon and Rosemary are great for neurological benefits.*

Daily Exercise:

*If you are at the Beginning of your brain injury recovery, 5 minutes is great on the recumbent bike. OR if you are further along in recovery, a walk, weight bearing exercise and yoga are great choices. Remember not too much. Start slow and build up to 20 minutes. *Consult with your Dr for your proper exercise prescription.*

Exercise Log:
_____
_____
_____
_____
_____

Did you get your Yoga stillness today?　　☐ yes　☐ no

This is your gateway to mental clarity and spiritual calm. Based on a centuries-old and scientifically proven pathway to health, Yoga is a gold star to your success. Great resources: Glo.com and Asanarebel.com

Daily Reflection:

Date: _____

Determination/noun:
the strength needed to succeed

I am grateful for ...

○ _____
○ _____
○ _____

Positive Affirmations

○ _____
○ _____
○ _____

Did you meditate? ☐ *yes* ☐ *no*
(At least 5 minutes, a great meditation APP: Calm.com)

Did you do the following?

Physical Therapy ☐ *yes* ☐ *no*
Occupational Therapy ☐ *yes* ☐ *no*
Speech Therapy ☐ *yes* ☐ *no*
Music Therapy ☐ *yes* ☐ *no*
Equine Therapy ☐ *yes* ☐ *no*
Cognitive Behavior Therapy ☐ *yes* ☐ *no*

How did you feel?

☐ *awesome* ☐ *okay* ☐ *not so good*

Did you get a breath of Fresh Air Today?

☐ *yes* ☐ *no*

Did you get your healthy 7-9 hrs of sleep?

☐ *yes* ☐ *no*

Naps:

☐ *1-2 hours* ☐ *2-4 hours* ☐ *other*

Listening to music

Listening to music you love will make your brain release more dopamine! The naturally occurring happy chemical. Make sure to listen to more of your favorite tunes!

Meals Today:

Be sure to add
Functional Foods in your diet

Breakfast
_____
_____

Snack
_____
_____

Lunch
_____
_____

Snack
_____
_____

Dinner
_____
_____

Snack
_____
_____

Did you Spice up your day with Turmeric?   ☐ yes   ☐ no

(Best for Neuroprotection)

Did you get your Rainbow Greens today?   ☐ yes   ☐ no

(Dark Leafy Green is best for Brain Health)

Did you get Nuts/Seeds today?   ☐ yes   ☐ no

Vitamins I took today _____

(Omega-3 Fatty Acid is best for Your Brain Power and keeping your brain healthy.)
Great Sources of Omega-3s: *Salmon, Oysters, Caviar, Flax Seeds, Chia Seeds, and Walnuts.*
Other Great Sources of Brain Power - *Vitamins: B1, B6, B12, C, E, Antioxidants, Beta Carotene and Probiotics.*

Reminder: Cinnamon and Rosemary are great for neurological benefits.

Daily Exercise:

*If you are at the Beginning of your brain injury recovery, 5 minutes is great on the recumbent bike. OR if you are further along in recovery, a walk, weight bearing exercise and yoga are great choices. Remember not too much. Start slow and build up to 20 minutes. *Consult with your Dr for your proper exercise prescription.*

Exercise Log:
_____
_____
_____
_____

Did you get your Yoga stillness today?   ☐ yes   ☐ no

This is your gateway to mental clarity and spiritual calm. Based on a centuries-old and scientifically proven pathway to health, Yoga is a gold star to your success. Great resources: Glo.com and Asanarebel.com

Daily Reflection:

Date: _____

I am grateful for ...

_____

_____

_____

Positive Affirmations

_____
_____
_____

Did you meditate? ☐ yes ☐ no
(At least 5 minutes, a great meditation APP: Calm.com)

Did you do the following?

Physical Therapy	☐ yes	☐ no
Occupational Therapy	☐ yes	☐ no
Speech Therapy	☐ yes	☐ no
Music Therapy	☐ yes	☐ no
Equine Therapy	☐ yes	☐ no
Cognitive Behavior Therapy	☐ yes	☐ no

How did you feel?

☐ *awesome*   ☐ *okay*   ☐ *not so good*

Did you get a breath of Fresh Air Today?

☐ yes   ☐ no

Did you get your healthy 7-9 hrs of sleep?

☐ yes   ☐ no

Naps:

☐ *1-2 hours*   ☐ *2-4 hours*   ☐ *other*

Listening to music

Listening to music you love will make your brain release more dopamine! The naturally occurring happy chemical. Make sure to listen to more of your favorite tunes!

Meals Today:

Be sure to add
Functional Foods in your diet

Breakfast
_____
_____

Snack
_____
_____

Lunch
_____
_____

Snack
_____
_____

Dinner
_____
_____

Snack
_____
_____

Did you Spice up your day with Turmeric? ☐ yes ☐ no

(Best for Neuroprotection)

Did you get your Rainbow Greens today? ☐ yes ☐ no

(Dark Leafy Green is best for Brain Health)

Did you get Nuts/Seeds today? ☐ yes ☐ no

Vitamins I took today _____

(Omega-3 Fatty Acid is best for Your Brain Power and keeping your brain healthy.)
Great Sources of Omega-3s: *Salmon, Oysters, Caviar, Flax Seeds, Chia Seeds, and Walnuts.*
Other Great Sources of Brain Power - *Vitamins: B1, B6, B12, C, E, Antioxidants, Beta Carotene and Probiotics.*

Reminder: Cinnamon and Rosemary are great for neurological benefits.

Daily Exercise:

*If you are at the Beginning of your brain injury recovery, 5 minutes is great on the recumbent bike. OR if you are further along in recovery, a walk, weight bearing exercise and yoga are great choices. Remember not too much. Start slow and build up to 20 minutes. *Consult with your Dr for your proper exercise prescription.*

Exercise Log:

_____
_____
_____
_____
_____

Did you get your Yoga stillness today? ☐ yes ☐ no

This is your gateway to mental clarity and spiritual calm. Based on a centuries-old and scientifically proven pathway to health, Yoga is a gold star to your success. Great resources: Glo.com and Asanarebel.com

Daily Reflection:

Date: _____

Tough times don't last; tough people do.
– Unknown

I am grateful for ...

☼ _____

☼ _____

☼ _____

Positive Affirmations

☼ _____

☼ _____

☼ _____

Did you meditate? ☐ yes ☐ no

(At least 5 minutes, a great meditation APP: Calm.com)

Did you do the following?

Physical Therapy ☐ yes ☐ no

Occupational Therapy ☐ yes ☐ no

Speech Therapy ☐ yes ☐ no

Music Therapy ☐ yes ☐ no

Equine Therapy ☐ yes ☐ no

Cognitive Behavior Therapy ☐ yes ☐ no

How did you feel?

☐ awesome   ☐ okay   ☐ not so good

Did you get a breath of Fresh Air Today?

☐ yes   ☐ no

Did you get your healthy 7-9 hrs of sleep?

☐ yes   ☐ no

Naps:

☐ 1-2 hours   ☐ 2-4 hours   ☐ other

Listening to music

Listening to music you love will make your brain release more dopamine! The naturally occurring happy chemical. Make sure to listen to more of your favorite tunes!

Meals Today:

Be sure to add
Functional Foods in your diet

Breakfast _____

_____

Snack _____

_____

Lunch _____

_____

Snack _____

_____

Dinner _____

_____

Snack _____

_____

Did you Spice up your day with Turmeric? ☐ yes ☐ no
(Best for Neuroprotection)

Did you get your Rainbow Greens today? ☐ yes ☐ no
(Dark Leafy Green is best for Brain Health)

Did you get Nuts/Seeds today? ☐ yes ☐ no

Vitamins I took today _____

(Omega-3 Fatty Acid is best for Your Brain Power and keeping your brain healthy.)
Great Sources of Omega-3s: *Salmon, Oysters, Caviar, Flax Seeds, Chia Seeds, and Walnuts.*
Other Great Sources of Brain Power – *Vitamins: B1, B6, B12, C, E, Antioxidants, Beta Carotene and Probiotics.*

Reminder: Cinnamon and Rosemary are great for neurological benefits.

Daily Exercise:

*If you are at the Beginning of your brain injury recovery, 5 minutes is great on the recumbent bike. OR if you are further along in recovery, a walk, weight bearing exercise and yoga are great choices. Remember not too much. Start slow and build up to 20 minutes. *Consult with your Dr for your proper exercise prescription.*

Exercise Log:
_____
_____
_____
_____

Did you get your Yoga stillness today? ☐ yes ☐ no

This is your gateway to mental clarity and spiritual calm. Based on a centuries-old and scientifically proven pathway to health, Yoga is a gold star to your success. Great resources: Glo.com and Asanarebel.com

Daily Reflection:

Date: _____

Life is short.
Spend it with friends who make you laugh
and feel loved.

I am grateful for ...

☼ _____
☼ _____
☼ _____

Positive Affirmations

☼ _____
☼ _____
☼ _____

Did you meditate?   ☐ yes   ☐ no
(At least 5 minutes, a great meditation APP: Calm.com)

Did you do the following?

Physical Therapy   ☐ yes   ☐ no
Occupational Therapy   ☐ yes   ☐ no
Speech Therapy   ☐ yes   ☐ no
Music Therapy   ☐ yes   ☐ no
Equine Therapy   ☐ yes   ☐ no
Cognitive Behavior Therapy ☐ yes   ☐ no

How did you feel?

☐ awesome   ☐ okay   ☐ not so good

Did you get a breath of Fresh Air Today?

☐ yes   ☐ no

Did you get your healthy 7-9 hrs of sleep?

☐ yes   ☐ no

Naps:

☐ 1-2 hours   ☐ 2-4 hours   ☐ other

Listening to music

Listening to music you love will make your
brain release more dopamine! The
naturally occurring happy chemical.
Make sure to listen to more of your favorite
tunes!

Meals Today:

Be sure to add
Functional Foods in your diet

Breakfast
_____
_____

Snack
_____
_____

Lunch
_____
_____

Snack
_____
_____

Dinner
_____
_____

Snack
_____
_____

Did you Spice up your day with Turmeric? ☐ yes ☐ no

(Best for Neuroprotection)

Did you get your Rainbow Greens today? ☐ yes ☐ no

(Dark Leafy Green is best for Brain Health)

Did you get Nuts/Seeds today? ☐ yes ☐ no

Vitamins I took today _____

(Omega-3 Fatty Acid is best for Your Brain Power and keeping your brain healthy.)
Great Sources of Omega-3s: *Salmon, Oysters, Caviar, Flax Seeds, Chia Seeds, and Walnuts.*
Other Great Sources of Brain Power - *Vitamins: B1, B6, B12, C, E, Antioxidants, Beta Carotene and Probiotics.*

> *Reminder: Cinnamon and Rosemary are great for neurological benefits.*

Daily Exercise:

*If you are at the Beginning of your brain injury recovery, 5 minutes is great on the recumbent bike. OR if you are further along in recovery, a walk, weight bearing exercise and yoga are great choices. Remember not too much. Start slow and build up to 20 minutes. *Consult with your Dr for your proper exercise prescription.*

Exercise Log:

_____
_____
_____
_____

Did you get your Yoga stillness today? ☐ yes ☐ no

This is your gateway to mental clarity and spiritual calm. Based on a centuries-old and scientifically proven pathway to health, Yoga is a gold star to your success. Great resources: Glo.com and Asanarebel.com

Daily Reflection:

Date: _____

Believe you can and you're halfway there.
- Theodore Roosevelt

I am grateful for ...

○ _____
○ _____
○ _____

Positive Affirmations

○ _____
○ _____
○ _____

Did you meditate? ☐ yes ☐ no
(At least 5 minutes, a great meditation APP: Calm.com)

Did you do the following?

Physical Therapy ☐ yes ☐ no
Occupational Therapy ☐ yes ☐ no
Speech Therapy ☐ yes ☐ no
Music Therapy ☐ yes ☐ no
Equine Therapy ☐ yes ☐ no
Cognitive Behavior Therapy ☐ yes ☐ no

How did you feel?

☐ awesome ☐ okay ☐ not so good

Did you get a breath of Fresh Air Today?

☐ yes ☐ no

Did you get your healthy 7-9 hrs of sleep?

☐ yes ☐ no

Naps:

☐ 1-2 hours ☐ 2-4 hours ☐ other

Listening to music

Listening to music you love will make your brain release more dopamine! The naturally occurring happy chemical. Make sure to listen to more of your favorite tunes!

Meals Today:

Be sure to add
Functional Foods in your diet

Breakfast
_____

Snack
_____

Lunch
_____

Snack
_____

Dinner
_____

Snack
_____

Did you Spice up your day with Turmeric? ☐ yes ☐ no
(Best for Neuroprotection)

Did you get your Rainbow Greens today? ☐ yes ☐ no
(Dark Leafy Green is best for Brain Health)

Did you get Nuts/Seeds today? ☐ yes ☐ no

Vitamins I took today _____

(Omega-3 Fatty Acid is best for Your Brain Power and keeping your brain healthy.)
Great Sources of Omega-3s: *Salmon, Oysters, Caviar, Flax Seeds, Chia Seeds, and Walnuts.*
Other Great Sources of Brain Power *– Vitamins: B1, B6, B12, C, E, Antioxidants, Beta Carotene and Probiotics.*

Reminder: Cinnamon and Rosemary are great for neurological benefits.

Daily Exercise:

*If you are at the Beginning of your brain injury recovery, 5 minutes is great on the recumbent bike. OR if you are further along in recovery, a walk, weight bearing exercise and yoga are great choices. Remember not too much. Start slow and build up to 20 minutes. *Consult with your Dr for your proper exercise prescription.*

Exercise Log:
_____
_____
_____
_____

Did you get your Yoga stillness today? ☐ yes ☐ no

This is your gateway to mental clarity and spiritual calm. Based on a centuries-old and scientifically proven pathway to health. Yoga is a gold star to your success. Great resources: Glo.com and Asanarebel.com

Daily Reflection:

Date: _____

I have missed more than 9000 shots. I've lost 300 games.
26 times I have missed the game winning shot.
I have failed over again in my life. That is why I succeed.
– Michael Jordan

I am grateful for ...

○ _____

○ _____

○ _____

Positive Affirmations

○ _____

○ _____

○ _____

Did you meditate? ☐ yes ☐ no

(At least 5 minutes, a great meditation APP: Calm.com)

Did you do the following?

Physical Therapy ☐ yes ☐ no

Occupational Therapy ☐ yes ☐ no

Speech Therapy ☐ yes ☐ no

Music Therapy ☐ yes ☐ no

Equine Therapy ☐ yes ☐ no

Cognitive Behavior Therapy ☐ yes ☐ no

How did you feel?

☐ awesome ☐ okay ☐ not so good

Did you get a breath of Fresh Air Today?

☐ yes ☐ no

Did you get your healthy 7-9 hrs of sleep?

☐ yes ☐ no

Naps:

☐ 1-2 hours ☐ 2-4 hours ☐ other

Listening to music

Listening to music you love will make your brain release more dopamine! The naturally occurring happy chemical. Make sure to listen to more of your favorite tunes!

Meals Today:

Be sure to add Functional Foods in your diet

Breakfast _____

_____

Snack _____

_____

Lunch _____

_____

Snack _____

_____

Dinner _____

_____

Snack _____

_____

Did you Spice up your day with Turmeric? ☐ yes ☐ no
(Best for Neuroprotection)

Did you get your Rainbow Greens today? ☐ yes ☐ no
(Dark Leafy Green is best for Brain Health)

Did you get Nuts/Seeds today? ☐ yes ☐ no

Vitamins I took today _____

(Omega-3 Fatty Acid is best for Your Brain Power and keeping your brain healthy.)
Great Sources of Omega-3s: *Salmon, Oysters, Caviar, Flax Seeds, Chia Seeds, and Walnuts.*
Other Great Sources of Brain Power *- Vitamins: B1, B6, B12, C, E, Antioxidants, Beta Carotene and Probiotics.*

Reminder: Cinnamon and Rosemary are great for neurological benefits.

Daily Exercise:

If you are at the Beginning of your brain injury recovery, 5 minutes is great on the recumbent bike. OR if you are further along in recovery, a walk, weight bearing exercise and yoga are great choices. Remember not too much. Start slow and build up to 20 minutes. *Consult with your Dr for your proper exercise prescription.

Exercise Log:
_____
_____
_____
_____
_____

Did you get your Yoga stillness today? ☐ yes ☐ no

This is your gateway to mental clarity and spiritual calm. Based on a centuries-old and scientifically proven pathway to health, Yoga is a gold star to your success. Great resources: Glo.com and Asanarebel.com

Daily Reflection:

Date: _____

I am grateful for ...

 _____
 _____
 _____

Positive Affirmations

_____
_____
_____

Did you meditate?   ☐ yes   ☐ no
(At least 5 minutes, a great meditation APP: Calm.com)

Did you do the following?

Physical Therapy   ☐ yes   ☐ no
Occupational Therapy   ☐ yes   ☐ no
Speech Therapy   ☐ yes   ☐ no
Music Therapy   ☐ yes   ☐ no
Equine Therapy   ☐ yes   ☐ no
Cognitive Behavior Therapy ☐ yes   ☐ no

How did you feel?

☐ awesome   ☐ okay   ☐ not so good

Did you get a breath of Fresh Air Today?

☐ yes   ☐ no

Did you get your healthy 7-9 hrs of sleep?

☐ yes   ☐ no

Naps:

☐ 1-2 hours   ☐ 2-4 hours   ☐ other

Listening to music
Listening to music you love will make your brain release more dopamine! The naturally occurring happy chemical. Make sure to listen to more of your favorite tunes!

Meals Today:

*Be sure to add
Functional Foods in your diet*

Breakfast
_____

Snack
_____

Lunch
_____

Snack
_____

Dinner
_____

Snack
_____

Did you Spice up your day with Turmeric? ☐ yes ☐ no

(Best for Neuroprotection)

Did you get your Rainbow Greens today? ☐ yes ☐ no

(Dark Leafy Green is best for Brain Health)

Did you get Nuts/Seeds today? ☐ yes ☐ no

Vitamins I took today _____

(Omega-3 Fatty Acid is best for Your Brain Power and keeping your brain healthy.)
Great Sources of Omega-3s: Salmon, Oysters, Caviar, Flax Seeds, Chia Seeds, and Walnuts.
Other Great Sources of Brain Power - Vitamins: B1, B6, B12, C, E, Antioxidants, Beta Carotene and Probiotics.

Reminder: Cinnamon and Rosemary are great for neurological benefits.

Daily Exercise:

*If you are at the Beginning of your brain injury recovery, 5 minutes is great on the recumbent bike. OR if you are further along in recovery, a walk, weight bearing exercise and yoga are great choices. Remember not too much. Start slow and build up to 20 minutes. *Consult with your Dr for your proper exercise prescription.*

Exercise Log:

_____
_____
_____
_____

Did you get your Yoga stillness today? ☐ yes ☐ no

This is your gateway to mental clarity and spiritual calm. Based on a centuries-old and scientifically proven pathway to health, Yoga is a gold star to your success. Great resources: Glo.com and Asanarebel.com

Daily Reflection:

Date: _____

Your attitude not your aptitude,
will determine your altitude.
- Zig Ziglar

I am grateful for ...

☼ _____
☼ _____
☼ _____

Positive Affirmations

☼ _____
☼ _____
☼ _____

Did you meditate? ☐ yes ☐ no

(At least 5 minutes, a great meditation APP: Calm.com)

Did you do the following?

Physical Therapy ☐ yes ☐ no

Occupational Therapy ☐ yes ☐ no

Speech Therapy ☐ yes ☐ no

Music Therapy ☐ yes ☐ no

Equine Therapy ☐ yes ☐ no

Cognitive Behavior Therapy ☐ yes ☐ no

How did you feel?

☐ awesome ☐ okay ☐ not so good

Did you get a breath of Fresh Air Today?

☐ yes ☐ no

Did you get your healthy 7-9 hrs of sleep?

☐ yes ☐ no

Naps:

☐ 1-2 hours ☐ 2-4 hours ☐ other

Listening to music

Listening to music you love will make your brain release more dopamine! The naturally occurring happy chemical. Make sure to listen to more of your favorite tunes!

Meals Today:

Be sure to add
Functional Foods in your diet

Breakfast
_____
_____

Snack
_____
_____

Lunch
_____
_____

Snack
_____
_____

Dinner
_____
_____

Snack
_____
_____

Did you Spice up your day with Turmeric?   ☐ yes   ☐ no

(Best for Neuroprotection)

Did you get your Rainbow Greens today?   ☐ yes   ☐ no

(Dark Leafy Green is best for Brain Health)

Did you get Nuts/Seeds today?   ☐ yes   ☐ no

Vitamins I took today _____

(Omega-3 Fatty Acid is best for Your Brain Power and keeping your brain healthy.)
Great Sources of Omega-3s: *Salmon, Oysters, Caviar, Flax Seeds, Chia Seeds, and Walnuts.*
Other Great Sources of Brain Power *– Vitamins: B1, B6, B12, C, E, Antioxidants, Beta Carotene and Probiotics.*

Reminder: Cinnamon and Rosemary are great for neurological benefits.

Daily Exercise:

*If you are at the Beginning of your brain injury recovery, 5 minutes is great on the recumbent bike. OR if you are further along in recovery, a walk, weight bearing exercise and yoga are great choices. Remember not too much. Start slow and build up to 20 minutes. *Consult with your Dr for your proper exercise prescription.*

Exercise Log:

_____

_____

_____

_____

Did you get your Yoga stillness today?   ☐ yes   ☐ no

This is your gateway to mental clarity and spiritual calm. Based on a centuries-old and scientifically proven pathway to health, Yoga is a gold star to your success. Great resources: Glo.com and Asanarebel.com

Daily Reflection:

Date: _____

Turn your wounds into wisdom.
- Oprah Winfrey

I am grateful for ...

☀ _____
☀ _____
☀ _____

Positive Affirmations

☀ _____
☀ _____
☀ _____

Did you meditate?　☐ yes　☐ no

(At least 5 minutes, a great meditation APP: Calm.com)

Did you do the following?

Physical Therapy　☐ yes　☐ no
Occupational Therapy　☐ yes　☐ no
Speech Therapy　☐ yes　☐ no
Music Therapy　☐ yes　☐ no
Equine Therapy　☐ yes　☐ no
Cognitive Behavior Therapy　☐ yes　☐ no

How did you feel?

☐ awesome　☐ okay　☐ not so good

Did you get a breath of Fresh Air Today?

☐ yes　☐ no

Did you get your healthy 7-9 hrs of sleep?

☐ yes　☐ no

Naps:

☐ 1-2 hours　☐ 2-4 hours　☐ other

Listening to music

Listening to music you love will make your brain release more dopamine! The naturally occurring happy chemical. Make sure to listen to more of your favorite tunes!

Meals Today:

Be sure to add
Functional Foods in your diet

Breakfast
_____
_____

Snack
_____
_____

Lunch
_____
_____

Snack
_____
_____

Dinner
_____
_____

Snack
_____
_____

Did you Spice up your day with Turmeric?　　　☐ yes　☐ no

(Best for Neuroprotection)

Did you get your Rainbow Greens today?　　　☐ yes　☐ no

(Dark Leafy Green is best for Brain Health)

Did you get Nuts/Seeds today?　　　☐ yes　☐ no

Vitamins I took today _____

(Omega-3 Fatty Acid is best for Your Brain Power and keeping your brain healthy.)
Great Sources of Omega-3s: *Salmon, Oysters, Caviar, Flax Seeds, Chia Seeds, and Walnuts.*
Other Great Sources of Brain Power *– Vitamins: B1, B6, B12, C, E, Antioxidants, Beta Carotene and Probiotics.*

Reminder: Cinnamon and Rosemary are great for neurological benefits.

Daily Exercise:

*If you are at the Beginning of your brain injury recovery, 5 minutes is great on the recumbent bike. OR if you are further along in recovery, a walk, weight bearing exercise and yoga are great choices. Remember not too much. Start slow and build up to 20 minutes. *Consult with your Dr for your proper exercise prescription.*

Exercise Log:

_____

_____

_____

_____

Did you get your Yoga stillness today?　　　☐ yes　☐ no

This is your gateway to mental clarity and spiritual calm. Based on a centuries-old and scientifically proven pathway to health, Yoga is a gold star to your success. Great resources: Glo.com and Asanarebel.com

Daily Reflection:

Date: _____

I am grateful for ...

☼ _____
☼ _____
☼ _____

Positive Affirmations

☼ _____
☼ _____
☼ _____

Did you meditate? ☐ yes ☐ no
(At least 5 minutes, a great meditation APP: Calm.com)

Did you do the following?

Physical Therapy   ☐ yes ☐ no
Occupational Therapy   ☐ yes ☐ no
Speech Therapy   ☐ yes ☐ no
Music Therapy   ☐ yes ☐ no
Equine Therapy   ☐ yes ☐ no
Cognitive Behavior Therapy ☐ yes ☐ no

How did you feel?

☐ awesome   ☐ okay   ☐ not so good

Did you get a breath of Fresh Air Today?

☐ yes   ☐ no

Did you get your healthy 7-9 hrs of sleep?

☐ yes   ☐ no

Naps:

☐ 1-2 hours   ☐ 2-4 hours   ☐ other

Listening to music

Listening to music you love will make your brain release more dopamine! The naturally occurring happy chemical. Make sure to listen to more of your favorite tunes!

Meals Today:

Be sure to add
Functional Foods in your diet

Breakfast
_____

Snack
_____

Lunch
_____

Snack
_____

Dinner
_____

Snack
_____

Did you Spice up your day with Turmeric? ☐ yes ☐ no
(Best for Neuroprotection)

Did you get your Rainbow Greens today? ☐ yes ☐ no
(Dark Leafy Green is best for Brain Health)

Did you get Nuts/Seeds today? ☐ yes ☐ no

Vitamins I took today _____

(Omega-3 Fatty Acid is best for Your Brain Power and keeping your brain healthy.)
Great Sources of Omega-3s: *Salmon, Oysters, Caviar, Flax Seeds, Chia Seeds, and Walnuts.*
Other Great Sources of Brain Power - *Vitamins: B1, B6, B12, C, E, Antioxidants, Beta Carotene and Probiotics.*

Reminder: Cinnamon and Rosemary are great for neurological benefits.

Daily Exercise:

*If you are at the Beginning of your brain injury recovery, 5 minutes is great on the recumbent bike. OR if you are further along in recovery, a walk, weight bearing exercise and yoga are great choices. Remember not too much. Start slow and build up to 20 minutes. *Consult with your Dr for your proper exercise prescription.*

Exercise Log:
_____
_____
_____
_____

Did you get your Yoga stillness today? ☐ yes ☐ no

This is your gateway to mental clarity and spiritual calm. Based on a centuries-old and scientifically proven pathway to health, Yoga is a gold star to your success. Great resources: Glo.com and Asanarebel.com

Daily Reflection:

Date: _____

*Our Brains Power of Plasticity is nothing
short of Amazing
- Kristin Abello*

I am grateful for ...

○ _____
○ _____
○ _____

Positive Affirmations

○ _____
○ _____
○ _____

Did you meditate?　☐ *yes*　☐ *no*
(At least 5 minutes, a great meditation APP: Calm.com)

Did you do the following?

Physical Therapy　　　　☐ *yes*　☐ *no*

Occupational Therapy　　☐ *yes*　☐ *no*

Speech Therapy　　　　　☐ *yes*　☐ *no*

Music Therapy　　　　　☐ *yes*　☐ *no*

Equine Therapy　　　　　☐ *yes*　☐ *no*

Cognitive Behavior Therapy ☐ *yes*　☐ *no*

How did you feel?

☐ *awesome*　☐ *okay*　☐ *not so good*

Did you get a breath of Fresh Air Today?

☐ *yes*　　☐ *no*

Did you get your healthy 7-9 hrs of sleep?

☐ *yes*　　☐ *no*

Naps:

☐ *1-2 hours*　☐ *2-4 hours*　☐ *other*

Listening to music
*Listening to music you love will make your
brain release more dopamine! The
naturally occurring happy chemical.
Make sure to listen to more of your favorite
tunes!*

Meals Today:

*Be sure to add
Functional Foods in your diet*

Breakfast
_____
_____

Snack
_____
_____

Lunch
_____
_____

Snack
_____
_____

Dinner
_____
_____

Snack
_____
_____

Did you Spice up your day with Turmeric?　　　　　　☐ yes　☐ no

(Best for Neuroprotection)

Did you get your Rainbow Greens today?　　　　　　☐ yes　☐ no

(Dark Leafy Green is best for Brain Health)

Did you get Nuts/Seeds today?　　　　　　　　☐ yes　☐ no

Vitamins I took today _____

(Omega-3 Fatty Acid is best for Your Brain Power and keeping your brain healthy.)
Great Sources of Omega-3s: *Salmon, Oysters, Caviar, Flax Seeds, Chia Seeds, and Walnuts.*
Other Great Sources of Brain Power *– Vitamins: B1, B6, B12, C, E, Antioxidants, Beta Carotene and Probiotics.*

Reminder: Cinnamon and Rosemary are great for neurological benefits.

Daily Exercise:

*If you are at the Beginning of your brain injury recovery, 5 minutes is great on the recumbent bike. OR if you are further along in recovery, a walk, weight bearing exercise and yoga are great choices. Remember not too much. Start slow and build up to 20 minutes. *Consult with your Dr for your proper exercise prescription.*

Exercise Log:
_____
_____
_____
_____

Did you get your Yoga stillness today?　　　　　　☐ yes　☐ no

This is your gateway to mental clarity and spiritual calm. Based on a centuries-old and scientifically proven pathway to health, Yoga is a gold star to your success. Great resources: Glo.com and Asanarebel.com

Daily Reflection:

Date: _____

You Can and You will.
- Unknown

I am grateful for ...

- ☀ _____
- ☀ _____
- ☀ _____

Positive Affirmations

- ☀ _____
- ☀ _____
- ☀ _____

Did you meditate?   ☐ yes   ☐ no
(At least 5 minutes, a great meditation APP: Calm.com)

Did you do the following?

Physical Therapy   ☐ yes   ☐ no

Occupational Therapy   ☐ yes   ☐ no

Speech Therapy   ☐ yes   ☐ no

Music Therapy   ☐ yes   ☐ no

Equine Therapy   ☐ yes   ☐ no

Cognitive Behavior Therapy ☐ yes   ☐ no

How did you feel?

☐ awesome   ☐ okay   ☐ not so good

Did you get a breath of Fresh Air Today?

☐ yes   ☐ no

Did you get your healthy 7-9 hrs of sleep?

☐ yes   ☐ no

Naps:

☐ 1-2 hours   ☐ 2-4 hours   ☐ other

Listening to music

Listening to music you love will make your brain release more dopamine! The naturally occurring happy chemical. Make sure to listen to more of your favorite tunes!

Meals Today:

Be sure to add
Functional Foods in your diet

Breakfast
_____
_____

Snack
_____
_____

Lunch
_____
_____

Snack
_____
_____

Dinner
_____
_____

Snack
_____
_____

Did you Spice up your day with Turmeric? ☐ yes ☐ no

(Best for Neuroprotection)

Did you get your Rainbow Greens today? ☐ yes ☐ no

(Dark Leafy Green is best for Brain Health)

Did you get Nuts/Seeds today? ☐ yes ☐ no

Vitamins I took today _____

(Omega-3 Fatty Acid is best for Your Brain Power and keeping your brain healthy.)
Great Sources of Omega-3s: *Salmon, Oysters, Caviar, Flax Seeds, Chia Seeds, and Walnuts.*
Other Great Sources of Brain Power *– Vitamins: B1, B6, B12, C, E, Antioxidants, Beta Carotene and Probiotics.*

Reminder: Cinnamon and Rosemary are great for neurological benefits.

Daily Exercise:

If you are at the Beginning of your brain injury recovery, 5 minutes is great on the recumbent bike. OR if you are further along in recovery, a walk, weight bearing exercise and yoga are great choices. Remember not too much. Start slow and build up to 20 minutes. *Consult with your Dr for your proper exercise prescription.

Exercise Log:
_____
_____
_____
_____

Did you get your Yoga stillness today? ☐ yes ☐ no

This is your gateway to mental clarity and spiritual calm. Based on a centuries-old and scientifically proven pathway to health, Yoga is a gold star to your success. Great resources: Glo.com and Asanarebel.com

Daily Reflection:

Date: _____

*I will give you back your health
and heal your wounds.
- Jeremiah (30:17)*

I am grateful for ...

☀ _____
☀ _____
☀ _____

Positive Affirmations

☀ _____
☀ _____
☀ _____

Did you meditate?   ☐ *yes*   ☐ *no*
(At least 5 minutes, a great meditation APP: Calm.com)

Did you do the following?

Physical Therapy	☐ *yes*	☐ *no*
Occupational Therapy	☐ *yes*	☐ *no*
Speech Therapy	☐ *yes*	☐ *no*
Music Therapy	☐ *yes*	☐ *no*
Equine Therapy	☐ *yes*	☐ *no*
Cognitive Behavior Therapy	☐ *yes*	☐ *no*

How did you feel?

☐ *awesome*   ☐ *okay*   ☐ *not so good*

Did you get a breath of Fresh Air Today?

☐ *yes*   ☐ *no*

Did you get your healthy 7-9 hrs of sleep?

☐ *yes*   ☐ *no*

Naps:

☐ *1-2 hours*   ☐ *2-4 hours*   ☐ *other*

Listening to music

Listening to music you love will make your brain release more dopamine! The naturally occurring happy chemical. Make sure to listen to more of your favorite tunes!

Meals Today:

*Be sure to add
Functional Foods in your diet*

Breakfast
_____
_____

Snack
_____
_____

Lunch
_____
_____

Snack
_____
_____

Dinner
_____
_____

Snack
_____
_____

Did you Spice up your day with Turmeric? ☐ yes ☐ no
(Best for Neuroprotection)

Did you get your Rainbow Greens today? ☐ yes ☐ no
(Dark Leafy Green is best for Brain Health)

Did you get Nuts/Seeds today? ☐ yes ☐ no

Vitamins I took today

(Omega-3 Fatty Acid is best for Your Brain Power and keeping your brain healthy.)
Great Sources of Omega-3s: *Salmon, Oysters, Caviar, Flax Seeds, Chia Seeds, and Walnuts.*
Other Great Sources of Brain Power *- Vitamins: B1, B6, B12, C, E, Antioxidants, Beta Carotene and Probiotics.*

Reminder: Cinnamon and Rosemary are great for neurological benefits.

Daily Exercise:

If you are at the Beginning of your brain injury recovery, 5 minutes is great on the recumbent bike. OR if you are further along in recovery, a walk, weight bearing exercise and yoga are great choices. Remember not too much. Start slow and build up to 20 minutes. *Consult with your Dr for your proper exercise prescription.

Exercise Log:

Did you get your Yoga stillness today? ☐ yes ☐ no

This is your gateway to mental clarity and spiritual calm. Based on a centuries-old and scientifically proven pathway to health, Yoga is a gold star to your success. Great resources: Glo.com and Asanarebel.com

Daily Reflection:

Date: _____

Things will get BETTER.
- Unknown

I am grateful for ...

☼ _____
☼ _____
☼ _____

Positive Affirmations

☼ _____
☼ _____
☼ _____

Did you meditate?   ☐ yes   ☐ no
(At least 5 minutes, a great meditation APP: Calm.com)

Did you do the following?

Physical Therapy   ☐ yes   ☐ no
Occupational Therapy   ☐ yes   ☐ no
Speech Therapy   ☐ yes   ☐ no
Music Therapy   ☐ yes   ☐ no
Equine Therapy   ☐ yes   ☐ no
Cognitive Behavior Therapy ☐ yes   ☐ no

How did you feel?

☐ awesome   ☐ okay   ☐ not so good

Did you get a breath of Fresh Air Today?

☐ yes   ☐ no

Did you get your healthy 7-9 hrs of sleep?

☐ yes   ☐ no

Naps:

☐ 1-2 hours   ☐ 2-4 hours   ☐ other

Listening to music

Listening to music you love will make your brain release more dopamine! The naturally occurring happy chemical. Make sure to listen to more of your favorite tunes!

Meals Today:

Be sure to add
Functional Foods in your diet

Breakfast
_____
_____

Snack
_____
_____

Lunch
_____
_____

Snack
_____
_____

Dinner
_____
_____

Snack
_____
_____

Did you Spice up your day with Turmeric?   ☐ yes   ☐ no
(Best for Neuroprotection)

Did you get your Rainbow Greens today?   ☐ yes   ☐ no
(Dark Leafy Green is best for Brain Health)

Did you get Nuts/Seeds today?   ☐ yes   ☐ no

Vitamins I took today _____

(Omega-3 Fatty Acid is best for Your Brain Power and keeping your brain healthy.)
Great Sources of Omega-3s: *Salmon, Oysters, Caviar, Flax Seeds, Chia Seeds, and Walnuts.*
Other Great Sources of Brain Power - *Vitamins: B1, B6, B12, C, E, Antioxidants, Beta Carotene and Probiotics.*

> *Reminder: Cinnamon and Rosemary are great for neurological benefits.*

Daily Exercise:

If you are at the Beginning of your brain injury recovery, 5 minutes is great on the recumbent bike. OR if you are further along in recovery, a walk, weight bearing exercise and yoga are great choices. Remember not too much. Start slow and build up to 20 minutes. *Consult with your Dr for your proper exercise prescription.

Exercise Log:
_____
_____
_____
_____

Did you get your Yoga stillness today?   ☐ yes   ☐ no

This is your gateway to mental clarity and spiritual calm. Based on a centuries-old and scientifically proven pathway to health, Yoga is a gold star to your success. Great resources: Glo.com and Asanarebel.com

Daily Reflection:

Date: _____

Let whatever you do today be enough.
- Unknown

I am grateful for ...	Positive Affirmations

☀ _____ ☀ _____

☀ _____ ☀ _____

☀ _____ ☀ _____

Did you meditate? ☐ yes ☐ no
(At least 5 minutes, a great meditation APP: Calm.com)

Did you do the following?

Physical Therapy ☐ yes ☐ no

Occupational Therapy ☐ yes ☐ no

Speech Therapy ☐ yes ☐ no

Music Therapy ☐ yes ☐ no

Equine Therapy ☐ yes ☐ no

Cognitive Behavior Therapy ☐ yes ☐ no

How did you feel?

☐ awesome   ☐ okay   ☐ not so good

Did you get a breath of Fresh Air Today?

☐ yes   ☐ no

Did you get your healthy 7-9 hrs of sleep?

☐ yes   ☐ no

Naps:

☐ 1-2 hours   ☐ 2-4 hours   ☐ other

Listening to music
Listening to music you love will make your brain release more dopamine! The naturally occurring happy chemical. Make sure to listen to more of your favorite tunes! ♫

Meals Today:

Be sure to add
Functional Foods in your diet

Breakfast _____
_____

Snack _____
_____

Lunch _____
_____

Snack _____
_____

Dinner _____
_____

Snack _____
_____
_____

Did you Spice up your day with Turmeric? ☐ yes ☐ no
(Best for Neuroprotection)

Did you get your Rainbow Greens today? ☐ yes ☐ no
(Dark Leafy Green is best for Brain Health)

Did you get Nuts/Seeds today? ☐ yes ☐ no

Vitamins I took today _____

(Omega-3 Fatty Acid is best for Your Brain Power and keeping your brain healthy.)
Great Sources of Omega-3s: *Salmon, Oysters, Caviar, Flax Seeds, Chia Seeds, and Walnuts.*
Other Great Sources of Brain Power - *Vitamins: B1, B6, B12, C, E, Antioxidants, Beta Carotene and Probiotics.*

Reminder: Cinnamon and Rosemary are great for neurological benefits.

Daily Exercise:

If you are at the Beginning of your brain injury recovery, 5 minutes is great on the recumbent bike. OR if you are further along in recovery, a walk, weight bearing exercise and yoga are great choices. Remember not too much. Start slow and build up to 20 minutes. *Consult with your Dr for your proper exercise prescription.

Exercise Log:
_____
_____
_____
_____

Did you get your Yoga stillness today? ☐ yes ☐ no

This is your gateway to mental clarity and spiritual calm. Based on a centuries-old and scientifically proven pathway to health, Yoga is a gold star to your success. Great resources: Glo.com and Asanarebel.com

Daily Reflection:

Date: _____

*Every accomplishment starts with
the decision to try.
- TBIHopeandInspiration.com*

I am grateful for ...

☼ _____
☼ _____
☼ _____

Positive Affirmations

☼ _____
☼ _____
☼ _____

Did you meditate?   ☐ yes   ☐ no

(At least 5 minutes, a great meditation APP: Calm.com)

Did you do the following?

Physical Therapy   ☐ yes   ☐ no

Occupational Therapy   ☐ yes   ☐ no

Speech Therapy   ☐ yes   ☐ no

Music Therapy   ☐ yes   ☐ no

Equine Therapy   ☐ yes   ☐ no

Cognitive Behavior Therapy ☐ yes   ☐ no

How did you feel?

☐ awesome   ☐ okay   ☐ not so good

Did you get a breath of Fresh Air Today?

☐ yes   ☐ no

Did you get your healthy 7-9 hrs of sleep?

☐ yes   ☐ no

Naps:

☐ *1-2 hours*   ☐ *2-4 hours*   ☐ *other*

Listening to music

Listening to music you love will make your brain release more dopamine! The naturally occurring happy chemical. Make sure to listen to more of your favorite tunes!

Meals Today:

*Be sure to add
Functional Foods in your diet*

Breakfast
_____

Snack
_____

Lunch
_____

Snack
_____

Dinner
_____

Snack
_____

Did you Spice up your day with Turmeric?   ☐ yes   ☐ no

(Best for Neuroprotection)

Did you get your Rainbow Greens today?   ☐ yes   ☐ no

(Dark Leafy Green is best for Brain Health)

Did you get Nuts/Seeds today?   ☐ yes   ☐ no

Vitamins I took today _____

(Omega-3 Fatty Acid is best for Your Brain Power and keeping your brain healthy.)
Great Sources of Omega-3s: *Salmon, Oysters, Caviar, Flax Seeds, Chia Seeds, and Walnuts.*
Other Great Sources of Brain Power *– Vitamins: B1, B6, B12, C, E, Antioxidants, Beta Carotene and Probiotics.*

> *Reminder: Cinnamon and Rosemary are great for neurological benefits.*

Daily Exercise:

*If you are at the Beginning of your brain injury recovery, 5 minutes is great on the recumbent bike. OR if you are further along in recovery, a walk, weight bearing exercise and yoga are great choices. Remember not too much. Start slow and build up to 20 minutes. *Consult with your Dr for your proper exercise prescription.*

Exercise Log:

_____

_____

_____

_____

_____

Did you get your Yoga stillness today?   ☐ yes   ☐ no

This is your gateway to mental clarity and spiritual calm. Based on a centuries-old and scientifically proven pathway to health, Yoga is a gold star to your success. Great resources: Glo.com and Asanarebel.com

Daily Reflection:

Date: _____

Choose to be optimistic.
It feels Better.
– TBIHopeandInspiration.com

I am grateful for ...

☼ _____
☼ _____
☼ _____

Did you meditate? ☐ yes ☐ no

(At least 5 minutes, a great meditation APP: Calm.com)

Did you do the following?

Physical Therapy ☐ yes ☐ no
Occupational Therapy ☐ yes ☐ no
Speech Therapy ☐ yes ☐ no
Music Therapy ☐ yes ☐ no
Equine Therapy ☐ yes ☐ no
Cognitive Behavior Therapy ☐ yes ☐ no

How did you feel?

☐ awesome ☐ okay ☐ not so good

Did you get a breath of Fresh Air Today?

☐ yes ☐ no

Did you get your healthy 7-9 hrs of sleep?

☐ yes ☐ no

Naps:

☐ 1-2 hours ☐ 2-4 hours ☐ other

Positive Affirmations

☼ _____
☼ _____
☼ _____

Listening to music

Listening to music you love will make your brain release more dopamine! The naturally occurring happy chemical. Make sure to listen to more of your favorite tunes!

Meals Today:

Be sure to add
Functional Foods in your diet

Breakfast
_____

Snack
_____

Lunch
_____

Snack
_____

Dinner
_____

Snack
_____

Did you Spice up your day with Turmeric? ☐ yes ☐ no
(Best for Neuroprotection)

Did you get your Rainbow Greens today? ☐ yes ☐ no
(Dark Leafy Green is best for Brain Health)

Did you get Nuts/Seeds today? ☐ yes ☐ no

Vitamins I took today _____

(Omega-3 Fatty Acid is best for Your Brain Power and keeping your brain healthy.)
Great Sources of Omega-3s: *Salmon, Oysters, Caviar, Flax Seeds, Chia Seeds, and Walnuts.*
Other Great Sources of Brain Power *- Vitamins: B1, B6, B12, C, E, Antioxidants, Beta Carotene and Probiotics.*

> *Reminder: Cinnamon and Rosemary are great for neurological benefits.*

Daily Exercise:

If you are at the Beginning of your brain injury recovery, 5 minutes is great on the recumbent bike. OR if you are further along in recovery, a walk, weight bearing exercise and yoga are great choices. Remember not too much. Start slow and build up to 20 minutes. *Consult with your Dr for your proper exercise prescription.

Exercise Log:
_____
_____
_____
_____

Did you get your Yoga stillness today? ☐ yes ☐ no

This is your gateway to mental clarity and spiritual calm. Based on a centuries-old and scientifically proven pathway to health, Yoga is a gold star to your success. Great resources: Glo.com and Asanarebel.com

Daily Reflection:

Date: _____

Believe. Hope. Courage.
You got this!
- Kristin Abello

I am grateful for ...

☀ _____

☀ _____

☀ _____

Positive Affirmations

☀ _____

☀ _____

☀ _____

Did you meditate?　　☐ yes　　☐ no

(At least 5 minutes, a great meditation APP: Calm.com)

Did you do the following?

Physical Therapy　　　　　　☐ yes　　☐ no

Occupational Therapy　　　　☐ yes　　☐ no

Speech Therapy　　　　　　☐ yes　　☐ no

Music Therapy　　　　　　　☐ yes　　☐ no

Equine Therapy　　　　　　☐ yes　　☐ no

Cognitive Behavior Therapy ☐ yes　　☐ no

How did you feel?

☐ awesome　　☐ okay　　☐ not so good

Did you get a breath of Fresh Air Today?

☐ yes　　　　☐ no

Did you get your healthy 7-9 hrs of sleep?

☐ yes　　　　☐ no

Naps:

☐ 1-2 hours　☐ 2-4 hours　☐ other

Listening to music

Listening to music you love will make your brain release more dopamine! The naturally occurring happy chemical. Make sure to listen to more of your favorite tunes!

Meals Today:

Be sure to add
Functional Foods in your diet

Breakfast
_____

_____

Snack
_____

_____

Lunch
_____

_____

Snack
_____

_____

Dinner
_____

_____

Snack
_____

_____

Did you Spice up your day with Turmeric? ☐ yes ☐ no

(Best for Neuroprotection)

Did you get your Rainbow Greens today? ☐ yes ☐ no

(Dark Leafy Green is best for Brain Health)

Did you get Nuts/Seeds today? ☐ yes ☐ no

Vitamins I took today _____

(Omega-3 Fatty Acid is best for Your Brain Power and keeping your brain healthy.)
Great Sources of Omega-3s: *Salmon, Oysters, Caviar, Flax Seeds, Chia Seeds, and Walnuts.*
Other Great Sources of Brain Power – *Vitamins: B1, B6, B12, C, E, Antioxidants, Beta Carotene and Probiotics.*

Reminder: Cinnamon and Rosemary are great for neurological benefits.

Daily Exercise:

*If you are at the Beginning of your brain injury recovery, 5 minutes is great on the recumbent bike. OR if you are further along in recovery, a walk, weight bearing exercise and yoga are great choices. Remember not too much. Start slow and build up to 20 minutes. *Consult with your Dr for your proper exercise prescription.*

Exercise Log:

Did you get your Yoga stillness today? ☐ yes ☐ no

This is your gateway to mental clarity and spiritual calm. Based on a centuries-old and scientifically proven pathway to health, Yoga is a gold star to your success. Great resources: Glo.com and Asanarebel.com

Daily Reflection:

Date: _____

I am grateful for ...

☀ _____

☀ _____

☀ _____

Positive Affirmations

☀ _____

☀ _____

☀ _____

Did you meditate? ☐ yes ☐ no

(At least 5 minutes, a great meditation APP: Calm.com)

Did you do the following?

Physical Therapy	☐ yes	☐ no
Occupational Therapy	☐ yes	☐ no
Speech Therapy	☐ yes	☐ no
Music Therapy	☐ yes	☐ no
Equine Therapy	☐ yes	☐ no
Cognitive Behavior Therapy	☐ yes	☐ no

How did you feel?

☐ *awesome*   ☐ *okay*   ☐ *not so good*

Did you get a breath of Fresh Air Today?

☐ *yes*   ☐ *no*

Did you get your healthy 7-9 hrs of sleep?

☐ *yes*   ☐ *no*

Naps:

☐ *1-2 hours*   ☐ *2-4 hours*   ☐ *other*

Listening to music

Listening to music you love will make your brain release more dopamine! The naturally occurring happy chemical. Make sure to listen to more of your favorite tunes!

Meals Today:

*Be sure to add
Functional Foods in your diet*

Breakfast
_____

_____

Snack
_____

_____

Lunch
_____

_____

Snack
_____

_____

Dinner
_____

_____

Snack
_____

_____

Did you Spice up your day with Turmeric? ☐ yes ☐ no
(Best for Neuroprotection)

Did you get your Rainbow Greens today? ☐ yes ☐ no
(Dark Leafy Green is best for Brain Health)

Did you get Nuts/Seeds today? ☐ yes ☐ no

Vitamins I took today _____

(Omega-3 Fatty Acid is best for Your Brain Power and keeping your brain healthy.)
Great Sources of Omega-3s: *Salmon, Oysters, Caviar, Flax Seeds, Chia Seeds, and Walnuts.*
Other Great Sources of Brain Power - *Vitamins: B1, B6, B12, C, E, Antioxidants, Beta Carotene and Probiotics.*

> *Reminder: Cinnamon and Rosemary are great for neurological benefits.*

Daily Exercise:

*If you are at the Beginning of your brain injury recovery, 5 minutes is great on the recumbent bike. OR if you are further along in recovery, a walk, weight bearing exercise and yoga are great choices. Remember not too much. Start slow and build up to 20 minutes. *Consult with your Dr for your proper exercise prescription.*

Exercise Log:
_____
_____
_____
_____

Did you get your Yoga stillness today? ☐ yes ☐ no

This is your gateway to mental clarity and spiritual calm. Based on a centuries-old and scientifically proven pathway to health, Yoga is a gold star to your success. Great resources: Glo.com and Asanarebel.com

Daily Reflection:

Date: _____

I am grateful for ...

☼ _____

☼ _____

☼ _____

Positive Affirmations

☼ _____

☼ _____

☼ _____

Did you meditate?   ☐ yes   ☐ no
(At least 5 minutes, a great meditation APP: Calm.com)

Did you do the following?

Physical Therapy   ☐ yes   ☐ no

Occupational Therapy   ☐ yes   ☐ no

Speech Therapy   ☐ yes   ☐ no

Music Therapy   ☐ yes   ☐ no

Equine Therapy   ☐ yes   ☐ no

Cognitive Behavior Therapy ☐ yes   ☐ no

How did you feel?

☐ awesome   ☐ okay   ☐ not so good

Did you get a breath of Fresh Air Today?

☐ yes   ☐ no

Did you get your healthy 7-9 hrs of sleep?

☐ yes   ☐ no

Naps:

☐ 1-2 hours   ☐ 2-4 hours   ☐ other

Listening to music

Listening to music you love will make your brain release more dopamine! The naturally occurring happy chemical. Make sure to listen to more of your favorite tunes!

Meals Today:

Be sure to add
Functional Foods in your diet

Breakfast
_____

Snack
_____

Lunch
_____

Snack
_____

Dinner
_____

Snack
_____

Did you Spice up your day with Turmeric?   ☐ yes   ☐ no
(Best for Neuroprotection)

Did you get your Rainbow Greens today?   ☐ yes   ☐ no
(Dark Leafy Green is best for Brain Health)

Did you get Nuts/Seeds today?   ☐ yes   ☐ no

Vitamins I took today _____

(Omega-3 Fatty Acid is best for Your Brain Power and keeping your brain healthy.)
Great Sources of Omega-3s: *Salmon, Oysters, Caviar, Flax Seeds, Chia Seeds, and Walnuts.*
Other Great Sources of Brain Power *- Vitamins: B1, B6, B12, C, E, Antioxidants, Beta Carotene and Probiotics.*

Reminder: Cinnamon and Rosemary are great for neurological benefits.

Daily Exercise:

*If you are at the Beginning of your brain injury recovery, 5 minutes is great on the recumbent bike. OR if you are further along in recovery, a walk, weight bearing exercise and yoga are great choices. Remember not too much. Start slow and build up to 20 minutes. *Consult with your Dr for your proper exercise prescription.*

Exercise Log:
_____
_____
_____
_____

Did you get your Yoga stillness today?   ☐ yes   ☐ no

This is your gateway to mental clarity and spiritual calm. Based on a centuries-old and scientifically proven pathway to health, Yoga is a gold star to your success. Great resources: Glo.com and Asanarebel.com

Daily Reflection:

Date: _____

I am grateful for ...

○ _____
○ _____
○ _____

Positive Affirmations

○ _____
○ _____
○ _____

Did you meditate?   ☐ yes   ☐ no
(At least 5 minutes, a great meditation APP: Calm.com)

Did you do the following?

Physical Therapy   ☐ yes   ☐ no
Occupational Therapy   ☐ yes   ☐ no
Speech Therapy   ☐ yes   ☐ no
Music Therapy   ☐ yes   ☐ no
Equine Therapy   ☐ yes   ☐ no
Cognitive Behavior Therapy ☐ yes   ☐ no

How did you feel?

☐ awesome   ☐ okay   ☐ not so good

Did you get a breath of Fresh Air Today?

☐ yes   ☐ no

Did you get your healthy 7-9 hrs of sleep?

☐ yes   ☐ no

Naps:

☐ 1-2 hours   ☐ 2-4 hours   ☐ other

Listening to music

Listening to music you love will make your brain release more dopamine! The naturally occurring happy chemical. Make sure to listen to more of your favorite tunes!

Meals Today:

Be sure to add
Functional Foods in your diet

Breakfast
_____
_____

Snack
_____
_____

Lunch
_____
_____

Snack
_____
_____

Dinner
_____
_____

Snack
_____
_____
_____

Did you Spice up your day with Turmeric?　　　☐ yes　☐ no

(Best for Neuroprotection)

Did you get your Rainbow Greens today?　　　☐ yes　☐ no

(Dark Leafy Green is best for Brain Health)

Did you get Nuts/Seeds today?　　　☐ yes　☐ no

Vitamins I took today　_____

(Omega-3 Fatty Acid is best for Your Brain Power and keeping your brain healthy.)
Great Sources of Omega-3s: *Salmon, Oysters, Caviar, Flax Seeds, Chia Seeds, and Walnuts.*
Other Great Sources of Brain Power *- Vitamins: B1, B6, B12, C, E, Antioxidants, Beta Carotene and Probiotics.*

> *Reminder: Cinnamon and Rosemary are great for neurological benefits.*

Daily Exercise:

If you are at the Beginning of your brain injury recovery, 5 minutes is great on the recumbent bike. OR if you are further along in recovery, a walk, weight bearing exercise and yoga are great choices. Remember not too much. Start slow and build up to 20 minutes. *Consult with your Dr for your proper exercise prescription.

Exercise Log:

_____
_____
_____
_____

Did you get your Yoga stillness today?　　　☐ yes　☐ no

This is your gateway to mental clarity and spiritual calm. Based on a centuries-old and scientifically proven pathway to health, Yoga is a gold star to your success. Great resources: Glo.com and Asanarebel.com

Daily Reflection:

Date: _____

Nothing is impossible.
The word itself says, I'm possible.
- Audrey Hepburn

I am grateful for ...

○ _____
○ _____
○ _____

Positive Affirmations

○ _____
○ _____
○ _____

Did you meditate? ☐ yes ☐ no
(At least 5 minutes, a great meditation APP: Calm.com)

Did you do the following?

Physical Therapy	☐ yes	☐ no
Occupational Therapy	☐ yes	☐ no
Speech Therapy	☐ yes	☐ no
Music Therapy	☐ yes	☐ no
Equine Therapy	☐ yes	☐ no
Cognitive Behavior Therapy	☐ yes	☐ no

How did you feel?

☐ *awesome* ☐ *okay* ☐ *not so good*

Did you get a breath of Fresh Air Today?

☐ *yes* ☐ *no*

Did you get your healthy 7-9 hrs of sleep?

☐ *yes* ☐ *no*

Naps:

☐ *1-2 hours* ☐ *2-4 hours* ☐ *other*

Listening to music

Listening to music you love will make your brain release more dopamine! The naturally occurring happy chemical. Make sure to listen to more of your favorite tunes!

Meals Today:

Be sure to add
Functional Foods in your diet

Breakfast
_____
_____

Snack
_____
_____

Lunch
_____
_____

Snack
_____
_____

Dinner
_____
_____

Snack
_____
_____

Did you Spice up your day with Turmeric? ☐ yes ☐ no
(Best for Neuroprotection)

Did you get your Rainbow Greens today? ☐ yes ☐ no
(Dark Leafy Green is best for Brain Health)

Did you get Nuts/Seeds today? ☐ yes ☐ no

Vitamins I took today _____

(Omega-3 Fatty Acid is best for Your Brain Power and keeping your brain healthy.)
Great Sources of Omega-3s: *Salmon, Oysters, Caviar, Flax Seeds, Chia Seeds, and Walnuts.*
Other Great Sources of Brain Power *– Vitamins: B1, B6, B12, C, E, Antioxidants, Beta Carotene and Probiotics.*

> *Reminder: Cinnamon and Rosemary are great for neurological benefits.*

Daily Exercise:

If you are at the Beginning of your brain injury recovery, 5 minutes is great on the recumbent bike. OR if you are further along in recovery, a walk, weight bearing exercise and yoga are great choices. Remember not too much. Start slow and build up to 20 minutes. *Consult with your Dr for your proper exercise prescription.

Exercise Log:
_____
_____
_____
_____
_____

Did you get your Yoga stillness today? ☐ yes ☐ no

This is your gateway to mental clarity and spiritual calm. Based on a centuries-old and scientifically proven pathway to health, Yoga is a gold star to your success. Great resources: Glo.com and Asanarebel.com

Daily Reflection:

Date: _____

> *God is all powerful and he can take care of us.*
> *– Wisdom (11:21)*

I am grateful for ...

☀ _____

☀ _____

☀ _____

Did you meditate? ☐ yes ☐ no
(At least 5 minutes, a great meditation APP: Calm.com)

Did you do the following?

Physical Therapy ☐ yes ☐ no

Occupational Therapy ☐ yes ☐ no

Speech Therapy ☐ yes ☐ no

Music Therapy ☐ yes ☐ no

Equine Therapy ☐ yes ☐ no

Cognitive Behavior Therapy ☐ yes ☐ no

How did you feel?

☐ awesome ☐ okay ☐ not so good

Did you get a breath of Fresh Air Today?

☐ yes ☐ no

Did you get your healthy 7-9 hrs of sleep?

☐ yes ☐ no

Naps:

☐ 1-2 hours ☐ 2-4 hours ☐ other

Positive Affirmations

☀ _____

☀ _____

☀ _____

Listening to music

Listening to music you love will make your brain release more dopamine! The naturally occurring happy chemical. Make sure to listen to more of your favorite tunes!

Meals Today:

Be sure to add Functional Foods in your diet

Breakfast
_____

Snack
_____

Lunch
_____

Snack
_____

Dinner
_____

Snack
_____
_____

Did you Spice up your day with Turmeric? ☐ yes ☐ no
(Best for Neuroprotection)

Did you get your Rainbow Greens today? ☐ yes ☐ no
(Dark Leafy Green is best for Brain Health)

Did you get Nuts/Seeds today? ☐ yes ☐ no

Vitamins I took today _____

(Omega-3 Fatty Acid is best for Your Brain Power and keeping your brain healthy.)
Great Sources of Omega-3s: *Salmon, Oysters, Caviar, Flax Seeds, Chia Seeds, and Walnuts.*
Other Great Sources of Brain Power – *Vitamins: B1, B6, B12, C, E, Antioxidants, Beta Carotene and Probiotics.*

Reminder: Cinnamon and Rosemary are great for neurological benefits.

Daily Exercise:

*If you are at the Beginning of your brain injury recovery, 5 minutes is great on the recumbent bike. OR if you are further along in recovery, a walk, weight bearing exercise and yoga are great choices. Remember not too much. Start slow and build up to 20 minutes. *Consult with your Dr for your proper exercise prescription.*

Exercise Log:
_____
_____
_____
_____
_____

Did you get your Yoga stillness today? ☐ yes ☐ no

This is your gateway to mental clarity and spiritual calm. Based on a centuries-old and scientifically proven pathway to health, Yoga is a gold star to your success. Great resources: Glo.com and Asanarebel.com

Daily Reflection:

Date: _____

YOU are Powerful!
You are more capable than you know, more brilliant than
you comprehend, and more powerful than you can even
begin to understand.
- Cyndie Spiegel

I am grateful for ...

○ _____
○ _____
○ _____

Positive Affirmations

○ _____
○ _____
○ _____

Did you meditate?   ☐ yes   ☐ no

(At least 5 minutes, a great meditation APP: Calm.com)

Did you do the following?

Physical Therapy   ☐ yes   ☐ no
Occupational Therapy   ☐ yes   ☐ no
Speech Therapy   ☐ yes   ☐ no
Music Therapy   ☐ yes   ☐ no
Equine Therapy   ☐ yes   ☐ no
Cognitive Behavior Therapy ☐ yes   ☐ no

How did you feel?

☐ *awesome*   ☐ *okay*   ☐ *not so good*

Did you get a breath of Fresh Air Today?

☐ *yes*   ☐ *no*

Did you get your healthy 7-9 hrs of sleep?

☐ *yes*   ☐ *no*

Naps:

☐ *1-2 hours*   ☐ *2-4 hours*   ☐ *other*

Listening to music

Listening to music you love will make your
brain release more dopamine! The
naturally occurring happy chemical.
Make sure to listen to more of your favorite
tunes!

Meals Today:

Be sure to add
Functional Foods in your diet

Breakfast
_____
_____

Snack
_____
_____

Lunch
_____
_____

Snack
_____
_____

Dinner
_____
_____

Snack
_____
_____

Did you Spice up your day with Turmeric? ☐ yes ☐ no
(Best for Neuroprotection)

Did you get your Rainbow Greens today? ☐ yes ☐ no
(Dark Leafy Green is best for Brain Health)

Did you get Nuts/Seeds today? ☐ yes ☐ no

Vitamins I took today _____

(Omega-3 Fatty Acid is best for Your Brain Power and keeping your brain healthy.)
Great Sources of Omega-3s: *Salmon, Oysters, Caviar, Flax Seeds, Chia Seeds, and Walnuts.*
Other Great Sources of Brain Power – *Vitamins: B1, B6, B12, C, E, Antioxidants, Beta Carotene and Probiotics.*

> *Reminder: Cinnamon and Rosemary are great for neurological benefits.*

Daily Exercise:

If you are at the Beginning of your brain injury recovery, 5 minutes is great on the recumbent bike. OR if you are further along in recovery, a walk, weight bearing exercise and yoga are great choices. Remember not too much. Start slow and build up to 20 minutes. *Consult with your Dr for your proper exercise prescription.

Exercise Log:
_____
_____
_____
_____

Did you get your Yoga stillness today? ☐ yes ☐ no

This is your gateway to mental clarity and spiritual calm. Based on a centuries-old and scientifically proven pathway to health, Yoga is a gold star to your success. Great resources: Glo.com and Asanarebel.com

Daily Reflection:

Date: _____

*You must do the things
you think you cannot do.
– Eleanor Roosevelt*

I am grateful for ...

○ _____
○ _____
○ _____

Positive Affirmations

○ _____
○ _____
○ _____

Did you meditate? ☐ yes ☐ no
(At least 5 minutes, a great meditation APP: Calm.com)

Did you do the following?

Physical Therapy ☐ yes ☐ no
Occupational Therapy ☐ yes ☐ no
Speech Therapy ☐ yes ☐ no
Music Therapy ☐ yes ☐ no
Equine Therapy ☐ yes ☐ no
Cognitive Behavior Therapy ☐ yes ☐ no

How did you feel?

☐ *awesome* ☐ *okay* ☐ *not so good*

Did you get a breath of Fresh Air Today?

☐ *yes* ☐ *no*

Did you get your healthy 7-9 hrs of sleep?

☐ *yes* ☐ *no*

Naps:

☐ *1-2 hours* ☐ *2-4 hours* ☐ *other*

Listening to music

Listening to music you love will make your brain release more dopamine! The naturally occurring happy chemical. Make sure to listen to more of your favorite tunes!

Meals Today:

*Be sure to add
Functional Foods in your diet*

Breakfast
_____
_____

Snack
_____
_____

Lunch
_____
_____

Snack
_____
_____

Dinner
_____
_____

Snack
_____
_____

Did you Spice up your day with Turmeric?　　　　☐ yes　☐ no
(Best for Neuroprotection)

Did you get your Rainbow Greens today?　　　　☐ yes　☐ no
(Dark Leafy Green is best for Brain Health)

Did you get Nuts/Seeds today?　　　　　　　　☐ yes　☐ no

Vitamins I took today _____

(Omega-3 Fatty Acid is best for Your Brain Power and keeping your brain healthy.)
Great Sources of Omega-3s: *Salmon, Oysters, Caviar, Flax Seeds, Chia Seeds, and Walnuts.*
Other Great Sources of Brain Power – *Vitamins: B1, B6, B12, C, E, Antioxidants, Beta Carotene and Probiotics.*

> *Reminder: Cinnamon and Rosemary are great for neurological benefits.*

Daily Exercise:

*If you are at the Beginning of your brain injury recovery, 5 minutes is great on the recumbent bike. OR if you are further along in recovery, a walk, weight bearing exercise and yoga are great choices. Remember not too much. Start slow and build up to 20 minutes. *Consult with your Dr for your proper exercise prescription.*

Exercise Log:
_____
_____
_____
_____

Did you get your Yoga stillness today?　　　　☐ yes　☐ no

This is your gateway to mental clarity and spiritual calm. Based on a centuries-old and scientifically proven pathway to health, Yoga is a gold star to your success. Great resources: Glo.com and Asanarebel.com

Daily Reflection:

Date: _____

I am grateful for ...

_____

_____

_____

Positive Affirmations

_____

_____

_____

Did you meditate?   ☐ yes   ☐ no
(At least 5 minutes, a great meditation APP: Calm.com)

Did you do the following?

Physical Therapy   ☐ yes   ☐ no

Occupational Therapy   ☐ yes   ☐ no

Speech Therapy   ☐ yes   ☐ no

Music Therapy   ☐ yes   ☐ no

Equine Therapy   ☐ yes   ☐ no

Cognitive Behavior Therapy ☐ yes   ☐ no

How did you feel?

☐ *awesome*   ☐ *okay*   ☐ *not so good*

Did you get a breath of Fresh Air Today?

☐ *yes*   ☐ *no*

Did you get your healthy 7-9 hrs of sleep?

☐ *yes*   ☐ *no*

Naps:

☐ *1-2 hours*   ☐ *2-4 hours*   ☐ *other*

Listening to music

Listening to music you love will make your brain release more dopamine! The naturally occurring happy chemical. Make sure to listen to more of your favorite tunes!

Meals Today:

Be sure to add
Functional Foods in your diet

Breakfast
_____

Snack
_____

Lunch
_____

Snack
_____

Dinner
_____

Snack
_____

Did you Spice up your day with Turmeric? ☐ yes ☐ no

(Best for Neuroprotection)

Did you get your Rainbow Greens today? ☐ yes ☐ no

(Dark Leafy Green is best for Brain Health)

Did you get Nuts/Seeds today? ☐ yes ☐ no

Vitamins I took today _____

(Omega-3 Fatty Acid is best for Your Brain Power and keeping your brain healthy.)
Great Sources of Omega-3s: *Salmon, Oysters, Caviar, Flax Seeds, Chia Seeds, and Walnuts.*
Other Great Sources of Brain Power *- Vitamins: B1, B6, B12, C, E, Antioxidants, Beta Carotene and Probiotics.*

> *Reminder: Cinnamon and Rosemary are great for neurological benefits.*

Daily Exercise:

*If you are at the Beginning of your brain injury recovery, 5 minutes is great on the recumbent bike. OR if you are further along in recovery, a walk, weight bearing exercise and yoga are great choices. Remember not too much. Start slow and build up to 20 minutes. *Consult with your Dr for your proper exercise prescription.*

Exercise Log:

_____

_____

_____

_____

Did you get your Yoga stillness today? ☐ yes ☐ no

This is your gateway to mental clarity and spiritual calm. Based on a centuries-old and scientifically proven pathway to health, Yoga is a gold star to your success. Great resources: Glo.com and Asanarebel.com

Daily Reflection:

Date: _____

> *The most wasted of days is one without laughter.*
> *– E.E. Cummings*

I am grateful for ...

○ _____
○ _____
○ _____

Positive Affirmations

○ _____
○ _____
○ _____

Did you meditate? ☐ yes ☐ no
(At least 5 minutes, a great meditation APP: Calm.com)

Did you do the following?

Physical Therapy ☐ yes ☐ no

Occupational Therapy ☐ yes ☐ no

Speech Therapy ☐ yes ☐ no

Music Therapy ☐ yes ☐ no

Equine Therapy ☐ yes ☐ no

Cognitive Behavior Therapy ☐ yes ☐ no

How did you feel?

☐ awesome ☐ okay ☐ not so good

Did you get a breath of Fresh Air Today?

☐ yes ☐ no

Did you get your healthy 7-9 hrs of sleep?

☐ yes ☐ no

Naps:

☐ 1-2 hours ☐ 2-4 hours ☐ other

Listening to music

Listening to music you love will make your brain release more dopamine! The naturally occurring happy chemical. Make sure to listen to more of your favorite tunes!

Meals Today:

Be sure to add Functional Foods in your diet

Breakfast
_____
_____

Snack
_____
_____

Lunch
_____
_____

Snack
_____
_____

Dinner
_____
_____

Snack
_____
_____

Did you Spice up your day with Turmeric? ☐ yes ☐ no
(Best for Neuroprotection)

Did you get your Rainbow Greens today? ☐ yes ☐ no
(Dark Leafy Green is best for Brain Health)

Did you get Nuts/Seeds today? ☐ yes ☐ no

Vitamins I took today _____

(Omega-3 Fatty Acid is best for Your Brain Power and keeping your brain healthy.)
Great Sources of Omega-3s: *Salmon, Oysters, Caviar, Flax Seeds, Chia Seeds, and Walnuts.*
Other Great Sources of Brain Power *- Vitamins: B1, B6, B12, C, E, Antioxidants, Beta Carotene and Probiotics.*

Reminder: Cinnamon and Rosemary are great for neurological benefits.

Daily Exercise:

*If you are at the Beginning of your brain injury recovery, 5 minutes is great on the recumbent bike. OR if you are further along in recovery, a walk, weight bearing exercise and yoga are great choices. Remember not too much. Start slow and build up to 20 minutes. *Consult with your Dr for your proper exercise prescription.*

Exercise Log:
_____
_____
_____
_____

Did you get your Yoga stillness today? ☐ yes ☐ no

This is your gateway to mental clarity and spiritual calm. Based on a centuries-old and scientifically proven pathway to health, Yoga is a gold star to your success. Great resources: Glo.com and Asanarebel.com

Daily Reflection:

Date: _____

I am grateful for ...

☀ _____

☀ _____

☀ _____

Positive Affirmations

☀ _____

☀ _____

☀ _____

Did you meditate? ☐ yes ☐ no

(At least 5 minutes, a great meditation APP: Calm.com)

Did you do the following?

Physical Therapy ☐ yes ☐ no

Occupational Therapy ☐ yes ☐ no

Speech Therapy ☐ yes ☐ no

Music Therapy ☐ yes ☐ no

Equine Therapy ☐ yes ☐ no

Cognitive Behavior Therapy ☐ yes ☐ no

How did you feel?

☐ awesome ☐ okay ☐ not so good

Did you get a breath of Fresh Air Today?

☐ yes ☐ no

Did you get your healthy 7-9 hrs of sleep?

☐ yes ☐ no

Naps:

☐ 1-2 hours ☐ 2-4 hours ☐ other

Listening to music

Listening to music you love will make your brain release more dopamine! The naturally occurring happy chemical. Make sure to listen to more of your favorite tunes!

Meals Today:

Be sure to add Functional Foods in your diet

Breakfast
_____

Snack
_____

Lunch
_____

Snack
_____

Dinner
_____

Snack
_____

Did you Spice up your day with Turmeric?   ☐ yes   ☐ no
(Best for Neuroprotection)

Did you get your Rainbow Greens today?   ☐ yes   ☐ no
(Dark Leafy Green is best for Brain Health)

Did you get Nuts/Seeds today?   ☐ yes   ☐ no

Vitamins I took today _____

(Omega-3 Fatty Acid is best for Your Brain Power and keeping your brain healthy.)
Great Sources of Omega-3s: *Salmon, Oysters, Caviar, Flax Seeds, Chia Seeds, and Walnuts.*
Other Great Sources of Brain Power - *Vitamins: B1, B6, B12, C, E, Antioxidants, Beta Carotene and Probiotics.*

> *Reminder: Cinnamon and Rosemary are great for neurological benefits.*

Daily Exercise:

If you are at the Beginning of your brain injury recovery, 5 minutes is great on the recumbent bike. OR if you are further along in recovery, a walk, weight bearing exercise and yoga are great choices. Remember not too much. Start slow and build up to 20 minutes. *Consult with your Dr for your proper exercise prescription.

Exercise Log:
_____
_____
_____
_____

Did you get your Yoga stillness today?   ☐ yes   ☐ no

This is your gateway to mental clarity and spiritual calm. Based on a centuries-old and scientifically proven pathway to health, Yoga is a gold star to your success. Great resources: Glo.com and Asanarebel.com

Daily Reflection:

Date: _____

> *Small Steps Everyday.*
> *- Unknown*

I am grateful for ...

○ _____

○ _____

○ _____

Positive Affirmations

○ _____

○ _____

○ _____

Did you meditate?   ☐ yes   ☐ no

(At least 5 minutes, a great meditation APP: Calm.com)

Did you do the following?

Physical Therapy   ☐ yes   ☐ no

Occupational Therapy   ☐ yes   ☐ no

Speech Therapy   ☐ yes   ☐ no

Music Therapy   ☐ yes   ☐ no

Equine Therapy   ☐ yes   ☐ no

Cognitive Behavior Therapy ☐ yes   ☐ no

How did you feel?

☐ *awesome*   ☐ *okay*   ☐ *not so good*

Did you get a breath of Fresh Air Today?

☐ *yes*   ☐ *no*

Did you get your healthy 7-9 hrs of sleep?

☐ *yes*   ☐ *no*

Naps:

☐ *1-2 hours*   ☐ *2-4 hours*   ☐ *other*

Listening to music

Listening to music you love will make your brain release more dopamine! The naturally occurring happy chemical. Make sure to listen to more of your favorite tunes!

Meals Today:

Be sure to add Functional Foods in your diet

Breakfast
_____
_____

Snack
_____
_____

Lunch
_____
_____

Snack
_____
_____

Dinner
_____
_____

Snack
_____
_____

Did you Spice up your day with Turmeric?　　　☐ yes　　☐ no

(Best for Neuroprotection)

Did you get your Rainbow Greens today?　　　☐ yes　　☐ no

(Dark Leafy Green is best for Brain Health)

Did you get Nuts/Seeds today?　　　　　　　☐ yes　　☐ no

Vitamins I took today _____

(Omega-3 Fatty Acid is best for Your Brain Power and keeping your brain healthy.)
Great Sources of Omega-3s: *Salmon, Oysters, Caviar, Flax Seeds, Chia Seeds, and Walnuts.*
Other Great Sources of Brain Power *– Vitamins: B1, B6, B12, C, E, Antioxidants, Beta Carotene and Probiotics.*

Reminder: Cinnamon and Rosemary are great for neurological benefits.

Daily Exercise:

*If you are at the Beginning of your brain injury recovery, 5 minutes is great on the recumbent bike. OR if you are further along in recovery, a walk, weight bearing exercise and yoga are great choices. Remember not too much. Start slow and build up to 20 minutes. *Consult with your Dr for your proper exercise prescription.*

Exercise Log:

_____

_____

_____

_____

Did you get your Yoga stillness today?　　　☐ yes　　☐ no

This is your gateway to mental clarity and spiritual calm. Based on a centuries-old and scientifically proven pathway to health, Yoga is a gold star to your success. Great resources: Glo.com and Asanarebel.com

Daily Reflection:

Date: _____

I am grateful for ...

○ _____
○ _____
○ _____

Positive Affirmations

○ _____
○ _____
○ _____

Did you meditate?   ☐ yes   ☐ no

(At least 5 minutes, a great meditation APP: Calm.com)

Did you do the following?

Physical Therapy   ☐ yes   ☐ no

Occupational Therapy   ☐ yes   ☐ no

Speech Therapy   ☐ yes   ☐ no

Music Therapy   ☐ yes   ☐ no

Equine Therapy   ☐ yes   ☐ no

Cognitive Behavior Therapy ☐ yes   ☐ no

How did you feel?

☐ awesome   ☐ okay   ☐ not so good

Did you get a breath of Fresh Air Today?

☐ yes   ☐ no

Did you get your healthy 7-9 hrs of sleep?

☐ yes   ☐ no

Naps:

☐ 1-2 hours   ☐ 2-4 hours   ☐ other

Listening to music

Listening to music you love will make your brain release more dopamine! The naturally occurring happy chemical. Make sure to listen to more of your favorite tunes!

Meals Today:

*Be sure to add
Functional Foods in your diet*

Breakfast
_____

Snack
_____

Lunch
_____

Snack
_____

Dinner
_____

Snack
_____

Did you Spice up your day with Turmeric? ☐ yes ☐ no
(Best for Neuroprotection)

Did you get your Rainbow Greens today? ☐ yes ☐ no
(Dark Leafy Green is best for Brain Health)

Did you get Nuts/Seeds today? ☐ yes ☐ no

Vitamins I took today _____

(Omega-3 Fatty Acid is best for Your Brain Power and keeping your brain healthy.)
Great Sources of Omega-3s: *Salmon, Oysters, Caviar, Flax Seeds, Chia Seeds, and Walnuts.*
Other Great Sources of Brain Power - *Vitamins: B1, B6, B12, C, E, Antioxidants, Beta Carotene and Probiotics.*

Reminder: Cinnamon and Rosemary are great for neurological benefits.

Daily Exercise:

If you are at the Beginning of your brain injury recovery, 5 minutes is great on the recumbent bike. OR if you are further along in recovery, a walk, weight bearing exercise and yoga are great choices. Remember not too much. Start slow and build up to 20 minutes. *Consult with your Dr for your proper exercise prescription.

Exercise Log:
_____
_____
_____
_____

Did you get your Yoga stillness today? ☐ yes ☐ no

This is your gateway to mental clarity and spiritual calm. Based on a centuries-old and scientifically proven pathway to health, Yoga is a gold star to your success. Great resources: Glo.com and Asanarebel.com

Daily Reflection:

Date: _____

> *Every end is a beginning.*
> *- Ralph Waldo Emerson*

I am grateful for ...

○ _____

○ _____

○ _____

Positive Affirmations

○ _____

○ _____

○ _____

Did you meditate? ☐ yes ☐ no
(At least 5 minutes, a great meditation APP: Calm.com)

Did you do the following?

Physical Therapy ☐ yes ☐ no

Occupational Therapy ☐ yes ☐ no

Speech Therapy ☐ yes ☐ no

Music Therapy ☐ yes ☐ no

Equine Therapy ☐ yes ☐ no

Cognitive Behavior Therapy ☐ yes ☐ no

How did you feel?

☐ awesome ☐ okay ☐ not so good

Did you get a breath of Fresh Air Today?

☐ yes ☐ no

Did you get your healthy 7-9 hrs of sleep?

☐ yes ☐ no

Naps:

☐ 1-2 hours ☐ 2-4 hours ☐ other

Listening to music

Listening to music you love will make your brain release more dopamine! The naturally occurring happy chemical. Make sure to listen to more of your favorite tunes!

Meals Today:

Be sure to add Functional Foods in your diet

Breakfast
_____

Snack
_____

Lunch
_____

Snack
_____

Dinner
_____

Snack
_____
_____

Did you Spice up your day with Turmeric?   ☐ yes   ☐ no
(Best for Neuroprotection)

Did you get your Rainbow Greens today?   ☐ yes   ☐ no
(Dark Leafy Green is best for Brain Health)

Did you get Nuts/Seeds today?   ☐ yes   ☐ no

Vitamins I took today _____

(Omega-3 Fatty Acid is best for Your Brain Power and keeping your brain healthy.)
Great Sources of Omega-3s: *Salmon, Oysters, Caviar, Flax Seeds, Chia Seeds, and Walnuts.*
Other Great Sources of Brain Power – *Vitamins: B1, B6, B12, C, E, Antioxidants, Beta Carotene and Probiotics.*

Reminder: Cinnamon and Rosemary are great for neurological benefits.

Daily Exercise:

*If you are at the Beginning of your brain injury recovery, 5 minutes is great on the recumbent bike. OR if you are further along in recovery, a walk, weight bearing exercise and yoga are great choices. Remember not too much. Start slow and build up to 20 minutes. *Consult with your Dr for your proper exercise prescription.*

Exercise Log:
_____
_____
_____
_____
_____

Did you get your Yoga stillness today?   ☐ yes   ☐ no

This is your gateway to mental clarity and spiritual calm. Based on a centuries-old and scientifically proven pathway to health, Yoga is a gold star to your success. Great resources: Glo.com and Asanarebel.com

Daily Reflection:

Date: _____

I am grateful for ...

- ☼ _____
- ☼ _____
- ☼ _____

Positive Affirmations

- ☼ _____
- ☼ _____
- ☼ _____

Did you meditate?   ☐ yes   ☐ no
(At least 5 minutes, a great meditation APP: Calm.com)

Did you do the following?

Physical Therapy	☐ yes	☐ no
Occupational Therapy	☐ yes	☐ no
Speech Therapy	☐ yes	☐ no
Music Therapy	☐ yes	☐ no
Equine Therapy	☐ yes	☐ no
Cognitive Behavior Therapy	☐ yes	☐ no

How did you feel?

☐ *awesome*   ☐ *okay*   ☐ *not so good*

Did you get a breath of Fresh Air Today?

☐ yes   ☐ no

Did you get your healthy 7-9 hrs of sleep?

☐ yes   ☐ no

Naps:

☐ *1-2 hours*   ☐ *2-4 hours*   ☐ *other*

Listening to music

Listening to music you love will make your brain release more dopamine! The naturally occurring happy chemical. Make sure to listen to more of your favorite tunes!

Meals Today:

Be sure to add Functional Foods in your diet

Breakfast
_____
_____

Snack
_____
_____

Lunch
_____
_____

Snack
_____
_____

Dinner
_____
_____

Snack
_____
_____

Did you Spice up your day with Turmeric? ☐ yes ☐ no
(Best for Neuroprotection)

Did you get your Rainbow Greens today? ☐ yes ☐ no
(Dark Leafy Green is best for Brain Health)

Did you get Nuts/Seeds today? ☐ yes ☐ no

Vitamins I took today _____

(Omega-3 Fatty Acid is best for Your Brain Power and keeping your brain healthy.)
Great Sources of Omega-3s: *Salmon, Oysters, Caviar, Flax Seeds, Chia Seeds, and Walnuts.*
Other Great Sources of Brain Power *- Vitamins: B1, B6, B12, C, E, Antioxidants, Beta Carotene and Probiotics.*

Reminder: Cinnamon and Rosemary are great for neurological benefits.

Daily Exercise:

*If you are at the Beginning of your brain injury recovery, 5 minutes is great on the recumbent bike. OR if you are further along in recovery, a walk, weight bearing exercise and yoga are great choices. Remember not too much. Start slow and build up to 20 minutes. *Consult with your Dr for your proper exercise prescription.*

Exercise Log:

Did you get your Yoga stillness today? ☐ yes ☐ no

This is your gateway to mental clarity and spiritual calm. Based on a centuries-old and scientifically proven pathway to health, Yoga is a gold star to your success. Great resources: Glo.com and Asanarebel.com

Daily Reflection:

Date: _____

High Five for a Job well done!

I am grateful for ...

○ _____
○ _____
○ _____

Positive Affirmations

○ _____
○ _____
○ _____

Did you meditate? ☐ yes ☐ no
(At least 5 minutes, a great meditation APP: Calm.com)

Did you do the following?

Physical Therapy ☐ yes ☐ no
Occupational Therapy ☐ yes ☐ no
Speech Therapy ☐ yes ☐ no
Music Therapy ☐ yes ☐ no
Equine Therapy ☐ yes ☐ no
Cognitive Behavior Therapy ☐ yes ☐ no

How did you feel?

☐ awesome ☐ okay ☐ not so good

Did you get a breath of Fresh Air Today?

☐ yes ☐ no

Did you get your healthy 7-9 hrs of sleep?

☐ yes ☐ no

Naps:

☐ 1-2 hours ☐ 2-4 hours ☐ other

Listening to music

Listening to music you love will make your brain release more dopamine! The naturally occurring happy chemical. Make sure to listen to more of your favorite tunes!

Meals Today:

*Be sure to add
Functional Foods in your diet*

Breakfast
_____
_____

Snack
_____
_____

Lunch
_____
_____

Snack
_____
_____

Dinner
_____
_____

Snack
_____
_____

Did you Spice up your day with Turmeric? ☐ yes ☐ no
(Best for Neuroprotection)

Did you get your Rainbow Greens today? ☐ yes ☐ no
(Dark Leafy Green is best for Brain Health)

Did you get Nuts/Seeds today? ☐ yes ☐ no

Vitamins I took today _____

(Omega-3 Fatty Acid is best for Your Brain Power and keeping your brain healthy.)
Great Sources of Omega-3s: *Salmon, Oysters, Caviar, Flax Seeds, Chia Seeds, and Walnuts.*
Other Great Sources of Brain Power *– Vitamins: B1, B6, B12, C, E, Antioxidants, Beta Carotene and Probiotics.*

Reminder: Cinnamon and Rosemary are great for neurological benefits.

Daily Exercise:

*If you are at the Beginning of your brain injury recovery, 5 minutes is great on the recumbent bike. OR if you are further along in recovery, a walk, weight bearing exercise and yoga are great choices. Remember not too much. Start slow and build up to 20 minutes. *Consult with your Dr for your proper exercise prescription.*

Exercise Log:
_____
_____
_____
_____

Did you get your Yoga stillness today? ☐ yes ☐ no

This is your gateway to mental clarity and spiritual calm. Based on a centuries-old and scientifically proven pathway to health, Yoga is a gold star to your success. Great resources: Glo.com and Asanarebel.com

Daily Reflection:

Date: _____

I am grateful for ...

☼ _____
☼ _____
☼ _____

Positive Affirmations

☼ _____
☼ _____
☼ _____

Did you meditate?   ☐ yes   ☐ no

(At least 5 minutes, a great meditation APP: Calm.com)

Did you do the following?

Physical Therapy   ☐ yes   ☐ no

Occupational Therapy   ☐ yes   ☐ no

Speech Therapy   ☐ yes   ☐ no

Music Therapy   ☐ yes   ☐ no

Equine Therapy   ☐ yes   ☐ no

Cognitive Behavior Therapy ☐ yes   ☐ no

How did you feel?

☐ *awesome*   ☐ *okay*   ☐ *not so good*

Did you get a breath of Fresh Air Today?

☐ *yes*   ☐ *no*

Did you get your healthy 7-9 hrs of sleep?

☐ *yes*   ☐ *no*

Naps:

☐ *1-2 hours*   ☐ *2-4 hours*   ☐ *other*

Listening to music

Listening to music you love will make your brain release more dopamine! The naturally occurring happy chemical. Make sure to listen to more of your favorite tunes!

Meals Today:

*Be sure to add
Functional Foods in your diet*

Breakfast
_____
_____

Snack
_____
_____

Lunch
_____
_____

Snack
_____
_____

Dinner
_____
_____

Snack
_____
_____

Did you Spice up your day with Turmeric?　　　□ yes　□ no

(Best for Neuroprotection)

Did you get your Rainbow Greens today?　　　□ yes　□ no

(Dark Leafy Green is best for Brain Health)

Did you get Nuts/Seeds today?　　　　　　　□ yes　□ no

Vitamins I took today _____

(Omega-3 Fatty Acid is best for Your Brain Power and keeping your brain healthy.)
Great Sources of Omega-3s: *Salmon, Oysters, Caviar, Flax Seeds, Chia Seeds, and Walnuts.*
Other Great Sources of Brain Power – *Vitamins: B1, B6, B12, C, E, Antioxidants, Beta Carotene and Probiotics.*

> *Reminder: Cinnamon and Rosemary are great for neurological benefits.*

Daily Exercise:

If you are at the Beginning of your brain injury recovery, 5 minutes is great on the recumbent bike. OR if you are further along in recovery, a walk, weight bearing exercise and yoga are great choices. Remember not too much. Start slow and build up to 20 minutes. *Consult with your Dr for your proper exercise prescription.

Exercise Log:

_____
_____
_____
_____

Did you get your Yoga stillness today?　　　□ yes　□ no

This is your gateway to mental clarity and spiritual calm. Based on a centuries-old and scientifically proven pathway to health, Yoga is a gold star to your success. Great resources: Glo.com and Asanarebel.com

Daily Reflection:

Date: _____

I am grateful for ...

 _____

 _____

 _____

Positive Affirmations

_____

_____

_____

Did you meditate? ☐ yes ☐ no

(At least 5 minutes, a great meditation APP: Calm.com)

Did you do the following?

Physical Therapy ☐ yes ☐ no

Occupational Therapy ☐ yes ☐ no

Speech Therapy ☐ yes ☐ no

Music Therapy ☐ yes ☐ no

Equine Therapy ☐ yes ☐ no

Cognitive Behavior Therapy ☐ yes ☐ no

How did you feel?

☐ awesome   ☐ okay   ☐ not so good

Did you get a breath of Fresh Air Today?

☐ yes   ☐ no

Did you get your healthy 7-9 hrs of sleep?

☐ yes   ☐ no

Naps:

☐ *1-2 hours*   ☐ *2-4 hours*   ☐ *other*

Listening to music

Listening to music you love will make your brain release more dopamine! The naturally occurring happy chemical. Make sure to listen to more of your favorite tunes!

Meals Today:

Be sure to add
Functional Foods in your diet

Breakfast
_____
_____

Snack
_____
_____

Lunch
_____
_____

Snack
_____
_____

Dinner
_____
_____

Snack
_____
_____

Did you Spice up your day with Turmeric?   ☐ yes   ☐ no
(Best for Neuroprotection)

Did you get your Rainbow Greens today?   ☐ yes   ☐ no
(Dark Leafy Green is best for Brain Health)

Did you get Nuts/Seeds today?   ☐ yes   ☐ no

Vitamins I took today _____

(Omega-3 Fatty Acid is best for Your Brain Power and keeping your brain healthy.)
Great Sources of Omega-3s: *Salmon, Oysters, Caviar, Flax Seeds, Chia Seeds, and Walnuts.*
Other Great Sources of Brain Power - *Vitamins: B1, B6, B12, C, E, Antioxidants, Beta Carotene and Probiotics.*

Reminder: Cinnamon and Rosemary are great for neurological benefits.

Daily Exercise:

*If you are at the Beginning of your brain injury recovery, 5 minutes is great on the recumbent bike. OR if you are further along in recovery, a walk, weight bearing exercise and yoga are great choices. Remember not too much. Start slow and build up to 20 minutes. *Consult with your Dr for your proper exercise prescription.*

Exercise Log:

Did you get your Yoga stillness today?   ☐ yes   ☐ no

This is your gateway to mental clarity and spiritual calm. Based on a centuries-old and scientifically proven pathway to health, Yoga is a gold star to your success. Great resources: Glo.com and Asanarebel.com

Daily Reflection:

Date: _____

Be too optimistic to scare, too positive to doubt,
and too determined to be defeated.
– Jim Kwik

I am grateful for ...

○ _____
○ _____
○ _____

Positive Affirmations

○ _____
○ _____
○ _____

Did you meditate? ☐ yes ☐ no

(At least 5 minutes, a great meditation APP: Calm.com)

Did you do the following?

Physical Therapy   ☐ yes   ☐ no
Occupational Therapy   ☐ yes   ☐ no
Speech Therapy   ☐ yes   ☐ no
Music Therapy   ☐ yes   ☐ no
Equine Therapy   ☐ yes   ☐ no
Cognitive Behavior Therapy ☐ yes ☐ no

How did you feel?

☐ awesome   ☐ okay   ☐ not so good

Did you get a breath of Fresh Air Today?

☐ yes   ☐ no

Did you get your healthy 7-9 hrs of sleep?

☐ yes   ☐ no

Naps:

☐ 1-2 hours   ☐ 2-4 hours   ☐ other

Listening to music

Listening to music you love will make your brain release more dopamine! The naturally occurring happy chemical. Make sure to listen to more of your favorite tunes!

Meals Today:

Be sure to add
Functional Foods in your diet

Breakfast
_____

Snack
_____

Lunch
_____

Snack
_____

Dinner
_____

Snack
_____
_____

Did you Spice up your day with Turmeric?　　　　　　☐ yes　☐ no
(Best for Neuroprotection)

Did you get your Rainbow Greens today?　　　　　　☐ yes　☐ no
(Dark Leafy Green is best for Brain Health)

Did you get Nuts/Seeds today?　　　　　　　　　　☐ yes　☐ no

Vitamins I took today _____

(Omega-3 Fatty Acid is best for Your Brain Power and keeping your brain healthy.)
Great Sources of Omega-3s: *Salmon, Oysters, Caviar, Flax Seeds, Chia Seeds, and Walnuts.*
Other Great Sources of Brain Power – *Vitamins: B1, B6, B12, C, E, Antioxidants, Beta Carotene and Probiotics.*

Reminder: Cinnamon and Rosemary are great for neurological benefits.

Daily Exercise:

*If you are at the Beginning of your brain injury recovery, 5 minutes is great on the recumbent bike. OR if you are further along in recovery, a walk, weight bearing exercise and yoga are great choices. Remember not too much. Start slow and build up to 20 minutes. *Consult with your Dr for your proper exercise prescription.*

Exercise Log:
_____
_____
_____
_____

Did you get your Yoga stillness today?　　　　　　☐ yes　☐ no

This is your gateway to mental clarity and spiritual calm. Based on a centuries-old and scientifically proven pathway to health, Yoga is a gold star to your success. Great resources: Glo.com and Asanarebel.com

Daily Reflection:

Date: _____

I am grateful for ...

○ _____
○ _____
○ _____

Positive Affirmations

○ _____
○ _____
○ _____

Did you meditate? ☐ yes ☐ no

(At least 5 minutes, a great meditation APP: Calm.com)

Did you do the following?

Physical Therapy	☐ yes	☐ no
Occupational Therapy	☐ yes	☐ no
Speech Therapy	☐ yes	☐ no
Music Therapy	☐ yes	☐ no
Equine Therapy	☐ yes	☐ no
Cognitive Behavior Therapy	☐ yes	☐ no

How did you feel?

☐ *awesome* ☐ *okay* ☐ *not so good*

Did you get a breath of Fresh Air Today?

☐ *yes* ☐ *no*

Did you get your healthy 7-9 hrs of sleep?

☐ *yes* ☐ *no*

Naps:

☐ *1-2 hours* ☐ *2-4 hours* ☐ *other*

Listening to music

Listening to music you love will make your brain release more dopamine! The naturally occurring happy chemical. Make sure to listen to more of your favorite tunes!

Meals Today:

Be sure to add
Functional Foods in your diet

Breakfast
_____

Snack
_____

Lunch
_____

Snack
_____

Dinner
_____

Snack
_____

Did you Spice up your day with Turmeric?　　☐ yes　　☐ no

(Best for Neuroprotection)

Did you get your Rainbow Greens today?　　☐ yes　　☐ no

(Dark Leafy Green is best for Brain Health)

Did you get Nuts/Seeds today?　　☐ yes　　☐ no

Vitamins I took today _____

(Omega-3 Fatty Acid is best for Your Brain Power and keeping your brain healthy.)
Great Sources of Omega-3s: *Salmon, Oysters, Caviar, Flax Seeds, Chia Seeds, and Walnuts.*
Other Great Sources of Brain Power – *Vitamins: B1, B6, B12, C, E, Antioxidants, Beta Carotene and Probiotics.*

Reminder: Cinnamon and Rosemary are great for neurological benefits.

Daily Exercise:

*If you are at the Beginning of your brain injury recovery, 5 minutes is great on the recumbent bike. OR if you are further along in recovery, a walk, weight bearing exercise and yoga are great choices. Remember not too much. Start slow and build up to 20 minutes. *Consult with your Dr for your proper exercise prescription.*

Exercise Log:

_____

_____

_____

_____

_____

Did you get your Yoga stillness today?　　☐ yes　　☐ no

This is your gateway to mental clarity and spiritual calm. Based on a centuries-old and scientifically proven pathway to health, Yoga is a gold star to your success. Great resources: Glo.com and Asanarebel.com

Daily Reflection:

Date: _____

As your body moves,
your brain grooves.
– Jim Kwik

I am grateful for ...

○ _____
○ _____
○ _____

Positive Affirmations

○ _____
○ _____
○ _____

Did you meditate? ☐ yes ☐ no
(At least 5 minutes, a great meditation APP: Calm.com)

Did you do the following?

Physical Therapy ☐ yes ☐ no
Occupational Therapy ☐ yes ☐ no
Speech Therapy ☐ yes ☐ no
Music Therapy ☐ yes ☐ no
Equine Therapy ☐ yes ☐ no
Cognitive Behavior Therapy ☐ yes ☐ no

How did you feel?

☐ *awesome*   ☐ *okay*   ☐ *not so good*

Did you get a breath of Fresh Air Today?

☐ *yes*   ☐ *no*

Did you get your healthy 7-9 hrs of sleep?

☐ *yes*   ☐ *no*

Naps:

☐ *1-2 hours* ☐ *2-4 hours* ☐ *other*

Listening to music

Listening to music you love will make your brain release more dopamine! The naturally occurring happy chemical. Make sure to listen to more of your favorite tunes!

Meals Today:

Be sure to add
Functional Foods in your diet

Breakfast
_____
_____

Snack
_____
_____

Lunch
_____
_____

Snack
_____
_____

Dinner
_____
_____

Snack
_____
_____

Did you Spice up your day with Turmeric?　　　　　☐ yes　☐ no

(Best for Neuroprotection)

Did you get your Rainbow Greens today?　　　　　☐ yes　☐ no

(Dark Leafy Green is best for Brain Health)

Did you get Nuts/Seeds today?　　　　　☐ yes　☐ no

Vitamins I took today _____

(Omega-3 Fatty Acid is best for Your Brain Power and keeping your brain healthy.)
Great Sources of Omega-3s: *Salmon, Oysters, Caviar, Flax Seeds, Chia Seeds, and Walnuts.*
Other Great Sources of Brain Power *– Vitamins: B1, B6, B12, C, E, Antioxidants, Beta Carotene and Probiotics.*

Reminder: Cinnamon and Rosemary are great for neurological benefits.

Daily Exercise:

If you are at the Beginning of your brain injury recovery, 5 minutes is great on the recumbent bike. OR if you are further along in recovery, a walk, weight bearing exercise and yoga are great choices. Remember not too much. Start slow and build up to 20 minutes. *Consult with your Dr for your proper exercise prescription.

Exercise Log:

_____

_____

_____

_____

Did you get your Yoga stillness today?　　　　　☐ yes　☐ no

This is your gateway to mental clarity and spiritual calm. Based on a centuries-old and scientifically proven pathway to health, Yoga is a gold star to your success. Great resources: Glo.com and Asanarebel.com

Daily Reflection:

Date: _____

I am grateful for ...

○ _____
○ _____
○ _____

Positive Affirmations

○ _____
○ _____
○ _____

Did you meditate?   ☐ yes   ☐ no

(At least 5 minutes, a great meditation APP: Calm.com)

Did you do the following?

Physical Therapy ☐ yes ☐ no
Occupational Therapy ☐ yes ☐ no
Speech Therapy ☐ yes ☐ no
Music Therapy ☐ yes ☐ no
Equine Therapy ☐ yes ☐ no
Cognitive Behavior Therapy ☐ yes ☐ no

How did you feel?

☐ awesome   ☐ okay   ☐ not so good

Did you get a breath of Fresh Air Today?

☐ yes   ☐ no

Did you get your healthy 7-9 hrs of sleep?

☐ yes   ☐ no

Naps:

☐ 1-2 hours   ☐ 2-4 hours   ☐ other

Listening to music

Listening to music you love will make your brain release more dopamine! The naturally occurring happy chemical. Make sure to listen to more of your favorite tunes!

Meals Today:

Be sure to add Functional Foods in your diet

Breakfast
_____

Snack
_____

Lunch
_____

Snack
_____

Dinner
_____

Snack
_____

Did you Spice up your day with Turmeric? ☐ yes ☐ no

(Best for Neuroprotection)

Did you get your Rainbow Greens today? ☐ yes ☐ no

(Dark Leafy Green is best for Brain Health)

Did you get Nuts/Seeds today? ☐ yes ☐ no

Vitamins I took today _____

(Omega-3 Fatty Acid is best for Your Brain Power and keeping your brain healthy.)
Great Sources of Omega-3s: *Salmon, Oysters, Caviar, Flax Seeds, Chia Seeds, and Walnuts.*
Other Great Sources of Brain Power – *Vitamins: B1, B6, B12, C, E, Antioxidants, Beta Carotene and Probiotics.*

Reminder: Cinnamon and Rosemary are great for neurological benefits.

Daily Exercise:

*If you are at the Beginning of your brain injury recovery, 5 minutes is great on the recumbent bike. OR if you are further along in recovery, a walk, weight bearing exercise and yoga are great choices. Remember not too much. Start slow and build up to 20 minutes. *Consult with your Dr for your proper exercise prescription.*

Exercise Log:

_____

_____

_____

_____

_____

Did you get your Yoga stillness today? ☐ yes ☐ no

This is your gateway to mental clarity and spiritual calm. Based on a centuries-old and scientifically proven pathway to health, Yoga is a gold star to your success. Great resources: Glo.com and Asanarebel.com

Daily Reflection:

Date: _____

There are only two ways to live your life. One is though nothing is a miracle. The other is as though everything is a miracle.
– Albert Einstein

I am grateful for ...

○ _____
○ _____
○ _____

Positive Affirmations

○ _____
○ _____
○ _____

Did you meditate?   ☐ yes   ☐ no
(At least 5 minutes, a great meditation APP: Calm.com)

Did you do the following?

Physical Therapy   ☐ yes   ☐ no
Occupational Therapy   ☐ yes   ☐ no
Speech Therapy   ☐ yes   ☐ no
Music Therapy   ☐ yes   ☐ no
Equine Therapy   ☐ yes   ☐ no
Cognitive Behavior Therapy ☐ yes   ☐ no

How did you feel?

☐ *awesome*   ☐ *okay*   ☐ *not so good*

Did you get a breath of Fresh Air Today?

☐ *yes*   ☐ *no*

Did you get your healthy 7-9 hrs of sleep?

☐ *yes*   ☐ *no*

Naps:

☐ *1-2 hours*   ☐ *2-4 hours*   ☐ *other*

Listening to music

Listening to music you love will make your brain release more dopamine! The naturally occurring happy chemical. Make sure to listen to more of your favorite tunes!

Meals Today:

Be sure to add
Functional Foods in your diet

Breakfast
_____

Snack
_____

Lunch
_____

Snack
_____

Dinner
_____

Snack
_____

Did you Spice up your day with Turmeric? ☐ yes ☐ no
(Best for Neuroprotection)

Did you get your Rainbow Greens today? ☐ yes ☐ no
(Dark Leafy Green is best for Brain Health)

Did you get Nuts/Seeds today? ☐ yes ☐ no

Vitamins I took today _____

(Omega-3 Fatty Acid is best for Your Brain Power and keeping your brain healthy.)
Great Sources of Omega-3s: *Salmon, Oysters, Caviar, Flax Seeds, Chia Seeds, and Walnuts.*
Other Great Sources of Brain Power *– Vitamins: B1, B6, B12, C, E, Antioxidants, Beta Carotene and Probiotics.*

Reminder: Cinnamon and Rosemary are great for neurological benefits.

Daily Exercise:

If you are at the Beginning of your brain injury recovery, 5 minutes is great on the recumbent bike. OR if you are further along in recovery, a walk, weight bearing exercise and yoga are great choices. Remember not too much. Start slow and build up to 20 minutes. *Consult with your Dr for your proper exercise prescription.

Exercise Log:
_____
_____
_____
_____

Did you get your Yoga stillness today? ☐ yes ☐ no

This is your gateway to mental clarity and spiritual calm. Based on a centuries-old and scientifically proven pathway to health, Yoga is a gold star to your success. Great resources: Glo.com and Asanarebel.com

Daily Reflection:

Date: _____

Take the first step in faith.
You don't have to see the whole staircase,
just take the first step.
– Martin Luther King, Jr.

I am grateful for ...

○ _____
○ _____
○ _____

Positive Affirmations

○ _____
○ _____
○ _____

Did you meditate? ☐ yes ☐ no

(At least 5 minutes, a great meditation APP: Calm.com)

Did you do the following?

Physical Therapy	☐ yes	☐ no
Occupational Therapy	☐ yes	☐ no
Speech Therapy	☐ yes	☐ no
Music Therapy	☐ yes	☐ no
Equine Therapy	☐ yes	☐ no
Cognitive Behavior Therapy	☐ yes	☐ no

How did you feel?

☐ awesome   ☐ okay   ☐ not so good

Did you get a breath of Fresh Air Today?

☐ yes   ☐ no

Did you get your healthy 7-9 hrs of sleep?

☐ yes   ☐ no

Naps:

☐ 1-2 hours   ☐ 2-4 hours   ☐ other

Listening to music

Listening to music you love will make your brain release more dopamine! The naturally occurring happy chemical. Make sure to listen to more of your favorite tunes!

Meals Today:

Be sure to add
Functional Foods in your diet

Breakfast
_____

Snack
_____

Lunch
_____

Snack
_____

Dinner
_____

Snack
_____
_____

Did you Spice up your day with Turmeric?　　☐ yes　☐ no

(Best for Neuroprotection)

Did you get your Rainbow Greens today?　　☐ yes　☐ no

(Dark Leafy Green is best for Brain Health)

Did you get Nuts/Seeds today?　　☐ yes　☐ no

Vitamins I took today　_____

(Omega-3 Fatty Acid is best for Your Brain Power and keeping your brain healthy.)
Great Sources of Omega-3s: *Salmon, Oysters, Caviar, Flax Seeds, Chia Seeds, and Walnuts.*
Other Great Sources of Brain Power – *Vitamins: B1, B6, B12, C, E, Antioxidants, Beta Carotene and Probiotics.*

Reminder: Cinnamon and Rosemary are great for neurological benefits.

Daily Exercise:

*If you are at the Beginning of your brain injury recovery, 5 minutes is great on the recumbent bike. OR if you are further along in recovery, a walk, weight bearing exercise and yoga are great choices. Remember not too much. Start slow and build up to 20 minutes. *Consult with your Dr for your proper exercise prescription.*

Exercise Log:
_____
_____
_____
_____

Did you get your Yoga stillness today?　　☐ yes　☐ no

This is your gateway to mental clarity and spiritual calm. Based on a centuries-old and scientifically proven pathway to health, Yoga is a gold star to your success. Great resources: Glo.com and Asanarebel.com

Daily Reflection:

Date: _____

I have a FULL Day of
FAITH
LOVE
FAMILY & FRIENDS

I am grateful for ...

○ _____
○ _____
○ _____

Positive Affirmations

○ _____
○ _____
○ _____

Did you meditate? ☐ yes ☐ no

(At least 5 minutes, a great meditation APP: Calm.com)

Did you do the following?

Physical Therapy   ☐ yes ☐ no
Occupational Therapy   ☐ yes ☐ no
Speech Therapy   ☐ yes ☐ no
Music Therapy   ☐ yes ☐ no
Equine Therapy   ☐ yes ☐ no
Cognitive Behavior Therapy ☐ yes ☐ no

How did you feel?

☐ awesome   ☐ okay   ☐ not so good

Did you get a breath of Fresh Air Today?

☐ yes   ☐ no

Did you get your healthy 7-9 hrs of sleep?

☐ yes   ☐ no

Naps:

☐ 1-2 hours   ☐ 2-4 hours   ☐ other

Listening to music

Listening to music you love will make your brain release more dopamine! The naturally occurring happy chemical. Make sure to listen to more of your favorite tunes!

Meals Today:

Be sure to add
Functional Foods in your diet

Breakfast
_____
_____

Snack
_____
_____

Lunch
_____
_____

Snack
_____
_____

Dinner
_____
_____

Snack
_____
_____

Did you Spice up your day with Turmeric? ☐ yes ☐ no
(Best for Neuroprotection)

Did you get your Rainbow Greens today? ☐ yes ☐ no
(Dark Leafy Green is best for Brain Health)

Did you get Nuts/Seeds today? ☐ yes ☐ no

Vitamins I took today _____

(Omega-3 Fatty Acid is best for Your Brain Power and keeping your brain healthy.)
Great Sources of Omega-3s: *Salmon, Oysters, Caviar, Flax Seeds, Chia Seeds, and Walnuts.*
Other Great Sources of Brain Power *- Vitamins: B1, B6, B12, C, E, Antioxidants, Beta Carotene and Probiotics.*

Reminder: Cinnamon and Rosemary are great for neurological benefits.

Daily Exercise:

*If you are at the Beginning of your brain injury recovery, 5 minutes is great on the recumbent bike. OR if you are further along in recovery, a walk, weight bearing exercise and yoga are great choices. Remember not too much. Start slow and build up to 20 minutes. *Consult with your Dr for your proper exercise prescription.*

Exercise Log:
_____
_____
_____
_____

Did you get your Yoga stillness today? ☐ yes ☐ no

This is your gateway to mental clarity and spiritual calm. Based on a centuries-old and scientifically proven pathway to health, Yoga is a gold star to your success. Great resources: Glo.com and Asanarebel.com

Daily Reflection:

Date: _____

BElieve in YOUrself.
Meditate and Visualize for 15 minutes today
creating the life you desire.

I am grateful for ...

○ _____

○ _____

○ _____

Positive Affirmations

○ _____

○ _____

○ _____

Did you meditate? ☐ yes ☐ no

(At least 5 minutes, a great meditation APP: Calm.com)

Did you do the following?

Physical Therapy ☐ yes ☐ no

Occupational Therapy ☐ yes ☐ no

Speech Therapy ☐ yes ☐ no

Music Therapy ☐ yes ☐ no

Equine Therapy ☐ yes ☐ no

Cognitive Behavior Therapy ☐ yes ☐ no

How did you feel?

☐ *awesome* ☐ *okay* ☐ *not so good*

Did you get a breath of Fresh Air Today?

☐ *yes* ☐ *no*

Did you get your healthy 7-9 hrs of sleep?

☐ *yes* ☐ *no*

Naps:

☐ *1-2 hours* ☐ *2-4 hours* ☐ *other*

Listening to music

Listening to music you love will make your brain release more dopamine! The naturally occurring happy chemical. Make sure to listen to more of your favorite tunes!

Meals Today:

Be sure to add
Functional Foods in your diet

Breakfast
_____
_____

Snack
_____
_____

Lunch
_____
_____

Snack
_____
_____

Dinner
_____
_____

Snack
_____
_____

Did you Spice up your day with Turmeric? ☐ yes ☐ no
(Best for Neuroprotection)

Did you get your Rainbow Greens today? ☐ yes ☐ no
(Dark Leafy Green is best for Brain Health)

Did you get Nuts/Seeds today? ☐ yes ☐ no

Vitamins I took today _____

(Omega-3 Fatty Acid is best for Your Brain Power and keeping your brain healthy.)
Great Sources of Omega-3s: *Salmon, Oysters, Caviar, Flax Seeds, Chia Seeds, and Walnuts.*
Other Great Sources of Brain Power *- Vitamins: B1, B6, B12, C, E, Antioxidants, Beta Carotene and Probiotics.*

> *Reminder: Cinnamon and Rosemary are great for neurological benefits.*

Daily Exercise:

*If you are at the Beginning of your brain injury recovery, 5 minutes is great on the recumbent bike. OR if you are further along in recovery, a walk, weight bearing exercise and yoga are great choices. Remember not too much. Start slow and build up to 20 minutes. *Consult with your Dr for your proper exercise prescription.*

Exercise Log:

_____
_____
_____
_____

Did you get your Yoga stillness today? ☐ yes ☐ no

This is your gateway to mental clarity and spiritual calm. Based on a centuries-old and scientifically proven pathway to health, Yoga is a gold star to your success. Great resources: Glo.com and Asanarebel.com

Daily Reflection:

Date: _____

> *Patience and perseverance have a magical effect before which difficulties disappear and obstacles vanish.*
> *– John Quincy Adams*

I am grateful for ...

 _____

☼ _____

☼ _____

Positive Affirmations

☼ _____

☼ _____

☼ _____

Did you meditate? ☐ yes ☐ no

(At least 5 minutes, a great meditation APP: Calm.com)

Did you do the following?

Physical Therapy ☐ yes ☐ no

Occupational Therapy ☐ yes ☐ no

Speech Therapy ☐ yes ☐ no

Music Therapy ☐ yes ☐ no

Equine Therapy ☐ yes ☐ no

Cognitive Behavior Therapy ☐ yes ☐ no

How did you feel?

☐ awesome ☐ okay ☐ not so good

Did you get a breath of Fresh Air Today?

☐ yes ☐ no

Did you get your healthy 7-9 hrs of sleep?

☐ yes ☐ no

Naps:

☐ 1-2 hours ☐ 2-4 hours ☐ other

Listening to music

Listening to music you love will make your brain release more dopamine! The naturally occurring happy chemical. Make sure to listen to more of your favorite tunes!

Meals Today:

*Be sure to add
Functional Foods in your diet*

Breakfast
_____
_____

Snack
_____
_____

Lunch
_____
_____

Snack
_____
_____

Dinner
_____
_____

Snack
_____
_____

Did you Spice up your day with Turmeric? ☐ yes ☐ no
(Best for Neuroprotection)

Did you get your Rainbow Greens today? ☐ yes ☐ no
(Dark Leafy Green is best for Brain Health)

Did you get Nuts/Seeds today? ☐ yes ☐ no

Vitamins I took today _____

(Omega-3 Fatty Acid is best for Your Brain Power and keeping your brain healthy.)
Great Sources of Omega-3s: *Salmon, Oysters, Caviar, Flax Seeds, Chia Seeds, and Walnuts.*
Other Great Sources of Brain Power – *Vitamins: B1, B6, B12, C, E, Antioxidants, Beta Carotene and Probiotics.*

Reminder: Cinnamon and Rosemary are great for neurological benefits.

Daily Exercise:

*If you are at the Beginning of your brain injury recovery, 5 minutes is great on the recumbent bike. OR if you are further along in recovery, a walk, weight bearing exercise and yoga are great choices. Remember not too much. Start slow and build up to 20 minutes. *Consult with your Dr for your proper exercise prescription.*

Exercise Log:
_____
_____
_____
_____

Did you get your Yoga stillness today? ☐ yes ☐ no

This is your gateway to mental clarity and spiritual calm. Based on a centuries-old and scientifically proven pathway to health, Yoga is a gold star to your success. Great resources: Glo.com and Asanarebel.com

Daily Reflection:

Date: _____

I am grateful for ...

☼ _____

☼ _____

☼ _____

Positive Affirmations

☼ _____

☼ _____

☼ _____

Did you meditate?   ☐ yes   ☐ no

(At least 5 minutes, a great meditation APP: Calm.com)

Did you do the following?

Physical Therapy   ☐ yes   ☐ no

Occupational Therapy   ☐ yes   ☐ no

Speech Therapy   ☐ yes   ☐ no

Music Therapy   ☐ yes   ☐ no

Equine Therapy   ☐ yes   ☐ no

Cognitive Behavior Therapy ☐ yes   ☐ no

How did you feel?

☐ *awesome*   ☐ *okay*   ☐ *not so good*

Did you get a breath of Fresh Air Today?

☐ *yes*   ☐ *no*

Did you get your healthy 7-9 hrs of sleep?

☐ *yes*   ☐ *no*

Naps:

☐ *1-2 hours*   ☐ *2-4 hours*   ☐ *other*

Listening to music

Listening to music you love will make your brain release more dopamine! The naturally occurring happy chemical. Make sure to listen to more of your favorite tunes!

♫

Meals Today:

*Be sure to add
Functional Foods in your diet*

Breakfast

_____

Snack

_____

Lunch

_____

Snack

_____

Dinner

_____

Snack

_____

Did you Spice up your day with Turmeric?　　　　　☐ yes　　☐ no

(Best for Neuroprotection)

Did you get your Rainbow Greens today?　　　　　☐ yes　　☐ no

(Dark Leafy Green is best for Brain Health)

Did you get Nuts/Seeds today?　　　　　　　　　☐ yes　　☐ no

Vitamins I took today _____

(Omega-3 Fatty Acid is best for Your Brain Power and keeping your brain healthy.)
Great Sources of Omega-3s: *Salmon, Oysters, Caviar, Flax Seeds, Chia Seeds, and Walnuts.*
Other Great Sources of Brain Power - *Vitamins: B1, B6, B12, C, E, Antioxidants, Beta Carotene and Probiotics.*

Reminder: Cinnamon and Rosemary are great for neurological benefits.

Daily Exercise:

*If you are at the Beginning of your brain injury recovery, 5 minutes is great on the recumbent bike. OR if you are further along in recovery, a walk, weight bearing exercise and yoga are great choices. Remember not too much. Start slow and build up to 20 minutes. *Consult with your Dr for your proper exercise prescription.*

Exercise Log:

_____

_____

_____

_____

Did you get your Yoga stillness today?　　　　　☐ yes　　☐ no

This is your gateway to mental clarity and spiritual calm. Based on a centuries-old and scientifically proven pathway to health, Yoga is a gold star to your success. Great resources: Glo.com and Asanarebel.com

Daily Reflection:

Date: _____

Our Faith can move mountains.
−Matthew 17:20

I am grateful for ...

☼ _____
☼ _____
☼ _____

Positive Affirmations

☼ _____
☼ _____
☼ _____

Did you meditate? ☐ yes ☐ no
(At least 5 minutes, a great meditation APP: Calm.com)

Did you do the following?

Physical Therapy ☐ yes ☐ no
Occupational Therapy ☐ yes ☐ no
Speech Therapy ☐ yes ☐ no
Music Therapy ☐ yes ☐ no
Equine Therapy ☐ yes ☐ no
Cognitive Behavior Therapy ☐ yes ☐ no

How did you feel?

☐ awesome   ☐ okay   ☐ not so good

Did you get a breath of Fresh Air Today?

☐ yes   ☐ no

Did you get your healthy 7-9 hrs of sleep?

☐ yes   ☐ no

Naps:

☐ 1-2 hours   ☐ 2-4 hours   ☐ other

Listening to music

Listening to music you love will make your brain release more dopamine! The naturally occurring happy chemical. Make sure to listen to more of your favorite tunes!

Meals Today:

Be sure to add
Functional Foods in your diet

Breakfast
_____
_____

Snack
_____
_____

Lunch
_____
_____

Snack
_____
_____

Dinner
_____
_____

Snack
_____
_____

Did you Spice up your day with Turmeric?   ☐ yes   ☐ no
(Best for Neuroprotection)

Did you get your Rainbow Greens today?   ☐ yes   ☐ no
(Dark Leafy Green is best for Brain Health)

Did you get Nuts/Seeds today?   ☐ yes   ☐ no

Vitamins I took today _____

(Omega-3 Fatty Acid is best for Your Brain Power and keeping your brain healthy.)
Great Sources of Omega-3s: *Salmon, Oysters, Caviar, Flax Seeds, Chia Seeds, and Walnuts.*
Other Great Sources of Brain Power – *Vitamins: B1, B6, B12, C, E, Antioxidants, Beta Carotene and Probiotics.*

Reminder: Cinnamon and Rosemary are great for neurological benefits.

Daily Exercise:

If you are at the Beginning of your brain injury recovery, 5 minutes is great on the recumbent bike. OR if you are further along in recovery, a walk, weight bearing exercise and yoga are great choices. Remember not too much. Start slow and build up to 20 minutes. *Consult with your Dr for your proper exercise prescription.

Exercise Log:

_____
_____
_____
_____

Did you get your Yoga stillness today?   ☐ yes   ☐ no

This is your gateway to mental clarity and spiritual calm. Based on a centuries-old and scientifically proven pathway to health, Yoga is a gold star to your success. Great resources: Glo.com and Asanarebel.com

Daily Reflection:

Date: _____

I am grateful for ...

○ _____

○ _____

○ _____

Positive Affirmations

○ _____

○ _____

○ _____

Did you meditate?   ☐ yes   ☐ no

(At least 5 minutes, a great meditation APP: Calm.com)

Did you do the following?

Physical Therapy   ☐ yes   ☐ no

Occupational Therapy   ☐ yes   ☐ no

Speech Therapy   ☐ yes   ☐ no

Music Therapy   ☐ yes   ☐ no

Equine Therapy   ☐ yes   ☐ no

Cognitive Behavior Therapy   ☐ yes   ☐ no

How did you feel?

☐ awesome   ☐ okay   ☐ not so good

Did you get a breath of Fresh Air Today?

☐ yes   ☐ no

Did you get your healthy 7-9 hrs of sleep?

☐ yes   ☐ no

Naps:

☐ 1-2 hours   ☐ 2-4 hours   ☐ other

Listening to music

Listening to music you love will make your brain release more dopamine! The naturally occurring happy chemical. Make sure to listen to more of your favorite tunes!

Meals Today:

*Be sure to add
Functional Foods in your diet*

Breakfast

_____

_____

Snack

_____

_____

Lunch

_____

_____

Snack

_____

_____

Dinner

_____

_____

Snack

_____

_____

Did you Spice up your day with Turmeric?   ☐ yes   ☐ no

(Best for Neuroprotection)

Did you get your Rainbow Greens today?   ☐ yes   ☐ no

(Dark Leafy Green is best for Brain Health)

Did you get Nuts/Seeds today?   ☐ yes   ☐ no

Vitamins I took today _____

(Omega-3 Fatty Acid is best for Your Brain Power and keeping your brain healthy.)
Great Sources of Omega-3s: *Salmon, Oysters, Caviar, Flax Seeds, Chia Seeds, and Walnuts.*
Other Great Sources of Brain Power – *Vitamins: B1, B6, B12, C, E, Antioxidants, Beta Carotene and Probiotics.*

Reminder: Cinnamon and Rosemary are great for neurological benefits.

Daily Exercise:

If you are at the Beginning of your brain injury recovery, 5 minutes is great on the recumbent bike. OR if you are further along in recovery, a walk, weight bearing exercise and yoga are great choices. Remember not too much. Start slow and build up to 20 minutes. *Consult with your Dr for your proper exercise prescription.

Exercise Log:
_____
_____
_____
_____

Did you get your Yoga stillness today?   ☐ yes   ☐ no

This is your gateway to mental clarity and spiritual calm. Based on a centuries-old and scientifically proven pathway to health, Yoga is a gold star to your success. Great resources: Glo.com and Asanarebel.com

Daily Reflection:

Date: _____

Sometimes there are days when your favorite thing to do is to be! Today let it Be! This is your only to do today. 99

I am grateful for ...

☀ _____

☀ _____

☀ _____

Positive Affirmations

☀ _____

☀ _____

☀ _____

Did you meditate? ☐ yes ☐ no

(At least 5 minutes, a great meditation APP: Calm.com)

Did you do the following?

Physical Therapy ☐ yes ☐ no

Occupational Therapy ☐ yes ☐ no

Speech Therapy ☐ yes ☐ no

Music Therapy ☐ yes ☐ no

Equine Therapy ☐ yes ☐ no

Cognitive Behavior Therapy ☐ yes ☐ no

How did you feel?

☐ awesome ☐ okay ☐ not so good

Did you get a breath of Fresh Air Today?

☐ yes ☐ no

Did you get your healthy 7-9 hrs of sleep?

☐ yes ☐ no

Naps:

☐ 1-2 hours ☐ 2-4 hours ☐ other

Listening to music

Listening to music you love will make your brain release more dopamine! The naturally occurring happy chemical. Make sure to listen to more of your favorite tunes!

Meals Today:

Be sure to add Functional Foods in your diet

Breakfast
_____
_____

Snack
_____
_____

Lunch
_____
_____

Snack
_____
_____

Dinner
_____
_____

Snack
_____
_____

Did you Spice up your day with Turmeric?   ☐ yes   ☐ no

(Best for Neuroprotection)

Did you get your Rainbow Greens today?   ☐ yes   ☐ no

(Dark Leafy Green is best for Brain Health)

Did you get Nuts/Seeds today?   ☐ yes   ☐ no

Vitamins I took today _____

(Omega-3 Fatty Acid is best for Your Brain Power and keeping your brain healthy.)
Great Sources of Omega-3s: *Salmon, Oysters, Caviar, Flax Seeds, Chia Seeds, and Walnuts.*
Other Great Sources of Brain Power *– Vitamins: B1, B6, B12, C, E, Antioxidants, Beta Carotene and Probiotics.*

Reminder: Cinnamon and Rosemary are great for neurological benefits.

Daily Exercise:

*If you are at the Beginning of your brain injury recovery, 5 minutes is great on the recumbent bike. OR if you are further along in recovery, a walk, weight bearing exercise and yoga are great choices. Remember not too much. Start slow and build up to 20 minutes. *Consult with your Dr for your proper exercise prescription.*

Exercise Log:

_____

_____

_____

_____

Did you get your Yoga stillness today?   ☐ yes   ☐ no

This is your gateway to mental clarity and spiritual calm. Based on a centuries-old and scientifically proven pathway to health, Yoga is a gold star to your success. Great resources: Glo.com and Asanarebel.com

Daily Reflection:

Date: _____

I am grateful for ...

☀ _____

☀ _____

☀ _____

Positive Affirmations

☀ _____

☀ _____

☀ _____

Did you meditate? ☐ yes ☐ no

(At least 5 minutes, a great meditation APP: Calm.com)

Did you do the following?

Physical Therapy	☐ yes	☐ no
Occupational Therapy	☐ yes	☐ no
Speech Therapy	☐ yes	☐ no
Music Therapy	☐ yes	☐ no
Equine Therapy	☐ yes	☐ no
Cognitive Behavior Therapy	☐ yes	☐ no

How did you feel?

☐ awesome ☐ okay ☐ not so good

Did you get a breath of Fresh Air Today?

☐ yes ☐ no

Did you get your healthy 7-9 hrs of sleep?

☐ yes ☐ no

Naps:

☐ *1-2 hours* ☐ *2-4 hours* ☐ *other*

Listening to music

Listening to music you love will make your brain release more dopamine! The naturally occurring happy chemical. Make sure to listen to more of your favorite tunes!

Meals Today:

Be sure to add Functional Foods in your diet

Breakfast
_____
_____

Snack
_____

Lunch
_____

Snack
_____

Dinner
_____

Snack
_____

Did you Spice up your day with Turmeric?　　　☐ yes　☐ no

(Best for Neuroprotection)

Did you get your Rainbow Greens today?　　　☐ yes　☐ no

(Dark Leafy Green is best for Brain Health)

Did you get Nuts/Seeds today?　　　☐ yes　☐ no

Vitamins I took today _____

(Omega-3 Fatty Acid is best for Your Brain Power and keeping your brain healthy.)
Great Sources of Omega-3s: *Salmon, Oysters, Caviar, Flax Seeds, Chia Seeds, and Walnuts.*
Other Great Sources of Brain Power *- Vitamins: B1, B6, B12, C, E, Antioxidants, Beta Carotene and Probiotics.*

> *Reminder: Cinnamon and Rosemary are great for neurological benefits.*

Daily Exercise:

*If you are at the Beginning of your brain injury recovery, 5 minutes is great on the recumbent bike. OR if you are further along in recovery, a walk, weight bearing exercise and yoga are great choices. Remember not too much. Start slow and build up to 20 minutes. *Consult with your Dr for your proper exercise prescription.*

Exercise Log:

_____

_____

_____

_____

Did you get your Yoga stillness today?　　　☐ yes　☐ no

This is your gateway to mental clarity and spiritual calm. Based on a centuries-old and scientifically proven pathway to health, Yoga is a gold star to your success. Great resources: Glo.com and Asanarebel.com

Daily Reflection:

Date: _____

I am grateful for …

○ _____

○ _____

○ _____

Positive Affirmations

○ _____

○ _____

○ _____

Did you meditate?   ☐ yes   ☐ no
(At least 5 minutes, a great meditation APP: Calm.com)

Did you do the following?

Physical Therapy   ☐ yes   ☐ no

Occupational Therapy   ☐ yes   ☐ no

Speech Therapy   ☐ yes   ☐ no

Music Therapy   ☐ yes   ☐ no

Equine Therapy   ☐ yes   ☐ no

Cognitive Behavior Therapy   ☐ yes   ☐ no

How did you feel?

☐ *awesome*   ☐ *okay*   ☐ *not so good*

Did you get a breath of Fresh Air Today?

☐ *yes*   ☐ *no*

Did you get your healthy 7-9 hrs of sleep?

☐ *yes*   ☐ *no*

Naps:

☐ *1-2 hours*   ☐ *2-4 hours*   ☐ *other*

Listening to music

Listening to music you love will make your brain release more dopamine! The naturally occurring happy chemical. Make sure to listen to more of your favorite tunes!

Meals Today:

Be sure to add
Functional Foods in your diet

Breakfast
_____

_____

Snack
_____

_____

Lunch
_____

_____

Snack
_____

_____

Dinner
_____

_____

Snack
_____

_____

Did you Spice up your day with Turmeric?   ☐ yes   ☐ no
(Best for Neuroprotection)

Did you get your Rainbow Greens today?   ☐ yes   ☐ no
(Dark Leafy Green is best for Brain Health)

Did you get Nuts/Seeds today?   ☐ yes   ☐ no

Vitamins I took today _____

(Omega-3 Fatty Acid is best for Your Brain Power and keeping your brain healthy.)
Great Sources of Omega-3s: *Salmon, Oysters, Caviar, Flax Seeds, Chia Seeds, and Walnuts.*
Other Great Sources of Brain Power *– Vitamins: B1, B6, B12, C, E, Antioxidants, Beta Carotene and Probiotics.*

Reminder: Cinnamon and Rosemary are great for neurological benefits.

Daily Exercise:

If you are at the Beginning of your brain injury recovery, 5 minutes is great on the recumbent bike. OR if you are further along in recovery, a walk, weight bearing exercise and yoga are great choices. Remember not too much. Start slow and build up to 20 minutes. *Consult with your Dr for your proper exercise prescription.

Exercise Log:
_____
_____
_____
_____

Did you get your Yoga stillness today?   ☐ yes   ☐ no

This is your gateway to mental clarity and spiritual calm. Based on a centuries-old and scientifically proven pathway to health, Yoga is a gold star to your success. Great resources: Glo.com and Asanarebel.com

Daily Reflection:

Date: _____

Repeat after me:
My situation is temporary;
Nothing is permanent.

I am grateful for ...

- ☀ _____
- ☀ _____
- ☀ _____

Positive Affirmations

- ☀ _____
- ☀ _____
- ☀ _____

Did you meditate?   ☐ yes   ☐ no

(At least 5 minutes, a great meditation APP: Calm.com)

Did you do the following?

Physical Therapy	☐ yes	☐ no
Occupational Therapy	☐ yes	☐ no
Speech Therapy	☐ yes	☐ no
Music Therapy	☐ yes	☐ no
Equine Therapy	☐ yes	☐ no
Cognitive Behavior Therapy	☐ yes	☐ no

How did you feel?

☐ awesome   ☐ okay   ☐ not so good

Did you get a breath of Fresh Air Today?

☐ yes   ☐ no

Did you get your healthy 7-9 hrs of sleep?

☐ yes   ☐ no

Naps:

☐ 1-2 hours   ☐ 2-4 hours   ☐ other

Listening to music

Listening to music you love will make your brain release more dopamine! The naturally occurring happy chemical. Make sure to listen to more of your favorite tunes!

Meals Today:

Be sure to add
Functional Foods in your diet

Breakfast
_____
_____

Snack
_____
_____

Lunch
_____
_____

Snack
_____
_____

Dinner
_____
_____

Snack
_____
_____

Did you Spice up your day with Turmeric?　　　☐ yes　☐ no

(Best for Neuroprotection)

Did you get your Rainbow Greens today?　　　☐ yes　☐ no

(Dark Leafy Green is best for Brain Health)

Did you get Nuts/Seeds today?　　　　　　　☐ yes　☐ no

Vitamins I took today _____

(Omega-3 Fatty Acid is best for Your Brain Power and keeping your brain healthy.)
Great Sources of Omega-3s: *Salmon, Oysters, Caviar, Flax Seeds, Chia Seeds, and Walnuts.*
Other Great Sources of Brain Power *– Vitamins: B1, B6, B12, C, E, Antioxidants, Beta Carotene and Probiotics.*

Reminder: Cinnamon and Rosemary are great for neurological benefits.

Daily Exercise:

*If you are at the Beginning of your brain injury recovery, 5 minutes is great on the recumbent bike. OR if you are further along in recovery, a walk, weight bearing exercise and yoga are great choices. Remember not too much. Start slow and build up to 20 minutes. *Consult with your Dr for your proper exercise prescription.*

Exercise Log:
_____
_____
_____
_____

Did you get your Yoga stillness today?　　　☐ yes　☐ no

This is your gateway to mental clarity and spiritual calm. Based on a centuries-old and scientifically proven pathway to health, Yoga is a gold star to your success. Great resources: Glo.com and Asanarebel.com

Daily Reflection:

Date: _____

> Congratulations!
> Healing everyday feels so good!

I am grateful for ...

☼ _____
☼ _____
☼ _____

Positive Affirmations

☼ _____
☼ _____
☼ _____

Did you meditate?   ☐ yes   ☐ no
(At least 5 minutes, a great meditation APP: Calm.com)

Did you do the following?

Physical Therapy   ☐ yes   ☐ no
Occupational Therapy   ☐ yes   ☐ no
Speech Therapy   ☐ yes   ☐ no
Music Therapy   ☐ yes   ☐ no
Equine Therapy   ☐ yes   ☐ no
Cognitive Behavior Therapy ☐ yes   ☐ no

How did you feel?

☐ awesome   ☐ okay   ☐ not so good

Did you get a breath of Fresh Air Today?

☐ yes   ☐ no

Did you get your healthy 7-9 hrs of sleep?

☐ yes   ☐ no

Naps:

☐ 1-2 hours   ☐ 2-4 hours   ☐ other

Listening to music

Listening to music you love will make your brain release more dopamine! The naturally occurring happy chemical. Make sure to listen to more of your favorite tunes!

Meals Today:

*Be sure to add
Functional Foods in your diet*

Breakfast
_____

Snack
_____

Lunch
_____

Snack
_____

Dinner
_____

Snack
_____

Did you Spice up your day with Turmeric? ☐ yes ☐ no

(Best for Neuroprotection)

Did you get your Rainbow Greens today? ☐ yes ☐ no

(Dark Leafy Green is best for Brain Health)

Did you get Nuts/Seeds today? ☐ yes ☐ no

Vitamins I took today _____

(Omega-3 Fatty Acid is best for Your Brain Power and keeping your brain healthy.)
Great Sources of Omega-3s: *Salmon, Oysters, Caviar, Flax Seeds, Chia Seeds, and Walnuts.*
Other Great Sources of Brain Power - *Vitamins: B1, B6, B12, C, E, Antioxidants, Beta Carotene and Probiotics.*

Reminder: Cinnamon and Rosemary are great for neurological benefits.

Daily Exercise:

*If you are at the Beginning of your brain injury recovery, 5 minutes is great on the recumbent bike. OR if you are further along in recovery, a walk, weight bearing exercise and yoga are great choices. Remember not too much. Start slow and build up to 20 minutes. *Consult with your Dr for your proper exercise prescription.*

Exercise Log:

_____

_____

_____

_____

Did you get your Yoga stillness today? ☐ yes ☐ no

This is your gateway to mental clarity and spiritual calm. Based on a centuries-old and scientifically proven pathway to health, Yoga is a gold star to your success. Great resources: Glo.com and Asanarebel.com

Daily Reflection:

Date: _____

> *Imagine. Believe. Achieve.*

I am grateful for ...

- ○ _____
- ○ _____
- ○ _____

Positive Affirmations

- ○ _____
- ○ _____
- ○ _____

Did you meditate?   ☐ yes   ☐ no
(At least 5 minutes, a great meditation APP: Calm.com)

Did you do the following?

Physical Therapy	☐ yes	☐ no
Occupational Therapy	☐ yes	☐ no
Speech Therapy	☐ yes	☐ no
Music Therapy	☐ yes	☐ no
Equine Therapy	☐ yes	☐ no
Cognitive Behavior Therapy	☐ yes	☐ no

How did you feel?

☐ awesome   ☐ okay   ☐ not so good

Did you get a breath of Fresh Air Today?

☐ yes   ☐ no

Did you get your healthy 7–9 hrs of sleep?

☐ yes   ☐ no

Naps:

☐ 1-2 hours   ☐ 2-4 hours   ☐ other

Listening to music

Listening to music you love will make your brain release more dopamine! The naturally occurring happy chemical. Make sure to listen to more of your favorite tunes!

Meals Today:

Be sure to add Functional Foods in your diet

Breakfast
_____

Snack
_____

Lunch
_____

Snack
_____

Dinner
_____

Snack
_____

Did you Spice up your day with Turmeric? ☐ yes ☐ no
(Best for Neuroprotection)

Did you get your Rainbow Greens today? ☐ yes ☐ no
(Dark Leafy Green is best for Brain Health)

Did you get Nuts/Seeds today? ☐ yes ☐ no

Vitamins I took today _____

(Omega-3 Fatty Acid is best for Your Brain Power and keeping your brain healthy.)
Great Sources of Omega-3s: *Salmon, Oysters, Caviar, Flax Seeds, Chia Seeds, and Walnuts.*
Other Great Sources of Brain Power *- Vitamins: B1, B6, B12, C, E, Antioxidants, Beta Carotene and Probiotics.*

Reminder: Cinnamon and Rosemary are great for neurological benefits.

Daily Exercise:

*If you are at the Beginning of your brain injury recovery, 5 minutes is great on the recumbent bike. OR if you are further along in recovery, a walk, weight bearing exercise and yoga are great choices. Remember not too much. Start slow and build up to 20 minutes. *Consult with your Dr for your proper exercise prescription.*

Exercise Log:
_____
_____
_____
_____

Did you get your Yoga stillness today? ☐ yes ☐ no

This is your gateway to mental clarity and spiritual calm. Based on a centuries-old and scientifically proven pathway to health, Yoga is a gold star to your success. Great resources: Glo.com and Asanarebel.com

Daily Reflection:

Date: _____

I am grateful for ...

 _____

 _____

 _____

Positive Affirmations

_____

_____

_____

Did you meditate? ☐ yes ☐ no
(At least 5 minutes, a great meditation APP: Calm.com)

Did you do the following?

Physical Therapy ☐ yes ☐ no

Occupational Therapy ☐ yes ☐ no

Speech Therapy ☐ yes ☐ no

Music Therapy ☐ yes ☐ no

Equine Therapy ☐ yes ☐ no

Cognitive Behavior Therapy ☐ yes ☐ no

How did you feel?

☐ *awesome* ☐ *okay* ☐ *not so good*

Did you get a breath of Fresh Air Today?

☐ *yes* ☐ *no*

Did you get your healthy 7-9 hrs of sleep?

☐ *yes* ☐ *no*

Naps:

☐ *1-2 hours* ☐ *2-4 hours* ☐ *other*

Listening to music

Listening to music you love will make your brain release more dopamine! The naturally occurring happy chemical. Make sure to listen to more of your favorite tunes!

Meals Today:

*Be sure to add
Functional Foods in your diet*

Breakfast

_____

Snack

_____

Lunch

_____

Snack

_____

Dinner

_____

Snack

_____

Did you Spice up your day with Turmeric?　　　☐ yes　☐ no

(Best for Neuroprotection)

Did you get your Rainbow Greens today?　　　☐ yes　☐ no

(Dark Leafy Green is best for Brain Health)

Did you get Nuts/Seeds today?　　　☐ yes　☐ no

Vitamins I took today _____

(Omega-3 Fatty Acid is best for Your Brain Power and keeping your brain healthy.)
Great Sources of Omega-3s: *Salmon, Oysters, Caviar, Flax Seeds, Chia Seeds, and Walnuts.*
Other Great Sources of Brain Power *- Vitamins: B1, B6, B12, C, E, Antioxidants, Beta Carotene and Probiotics.*

> *Reminder: Cinnamon and Rosemary are great for neurological benefits.*

Daily Exercise:

*If you are at the Beginning of your brain injury recovery, 5 minutes is great on the recumbent bike. OR if you are further along in recovery, a walk, weight bearing exercise and yoga are great choices. Remember not too much. Start slow and build up to 20 minutes. *Consult with your Dr for your proper exercise prescription.*

Exercise Log:

_____

_____

_____

_____

Did you get your Yoga stillness today?　　　☐ yes　☐ no

This is your gateway to mental clarity and spiritual calm. Based on a centuries-old and scientifically proven pathway to health, Yoga is a gold star to your success. Great resources: Glo.com and Asanarebel.com

Daily Reflection:

Date: _____

It matters if you don't give up.
- Stephen W. Hawking

I am grateful for ...

○ _____
○ _____
○ _____

Positive Affirmations

○ _____
○ _____
○ _____

Did you meditate? ☐ yes ☐ no
(At least 5 minutes, a great meditation APP: Calm.com)

Did you do the following?

Physical Therapy	☐ yes	☐ no
Occupational Therapy	☐ yes	☐ no
Speech Therapy	☐ yes	☐ no
Music Therapy	☐ yes	☐ no
Equine Therapy	☐ yes	☐ no
Cognitive Behavior Therapy	☐ yes	☐ no

How did you feel?

☐ awesome ☐ okay ☐ not so good

Did you get a breath of Fresh Air Today?

☐ yes ☐ no

Did you get your healthy 7-9 hrs of sleep?

☐ yes ☐ no

Naps:

☐ *1-2 hours* ☐ *2-4 hours* ☐ *other*

Listening to music

Listening to music you love will make your brain release more dopamine! The naturally occurring happy chemical. Make sure to listen to more of your favorite tunes! ♫

Meals Today:

Be sure to add
Functional Foods in your diet

Breakfast
_____
_____

Snack
_____
_____

Lunch
_____
_____

Snack
_____
_____

Dinner
_____
_____

Snack
_____
_____

Did you Spice up your day with Turmeric?   ☐ yes   ☐ no
(Best for Neuroprotection)

Did you get your Rainbow Greens today?   ☐ yes   ☐ no
(Dark Leafy Green is best for Brain Health)

Did you get Nuts/Seeds today?   ☐ yes   ☐ no

Vitamins I took today _____

(Omega-3 Fatty Acid is best for Your Brain Power and keeping your brain healthy.)
Great Sources of Omega-3s: *Salmon, Oysters, Caviar, Flax Seeds, Chia Seeds, and Walnuts.*
Other Great Sources of Brain Power *- Vitamins: B1, B6, B12, C, E, Antioxidants, Beta Carotene and Probiotics.*

> *Reminder: Cinnamon and Rosemary are great for neurological benefits.*

Daily Exercise:

*If you are at the Beginning of your brain injury recovery, 5 minutes is great on the recumbent bike. OR if you are further along in recovery, a walk, weight bearing exercise and yoga are great choices. Remember not too much. Start slow and build up to 20 minutes. *Consult with your Dr for your proper exercise prescription.*

Exercise Log:

_____
_____
_____
_____

Did you get your Yoga stillness today?   ☐ yes   ☐ no

This is your gateway to mental clarity and spiritual calm. Based on a centuries-old and scientifically proven pathway to health, Yoga is a gold star to your success. Great resources: Glo.com and Asanarebel.com

Daily Reflection:

Date: _____

I am grateful for ...

☼ _____

☼ _____

☼ _____

Positive Affirmations

☼ _____

☼ _____

☼ _____

Did you meditate? ☐ yes ☐ no
(At least 5 minutes, a great meditation APP: Calm.com)

Did you do the following?

Physical Therapy	☐ yes	☐ no
Occupational Therapy	☐ yes	☐ no
Speech Therapy	☐ yes	☐ no
Music Therapy	☐ yes	☐ no
Equine Therapy	☐ yes	☐ no
Cognitive Behavior Therapy	☐ yes	☐ no

How did you feel?

☐ awesome   ☐ okay   ☐ not so good

Did you get a breath of Fresh Air Today?

☐ yes   ☐ no

Did you get your healthy 7-9 hrs of sleep?

☐ yes   ☐ no

Naps:

☐ 1-2 hours   ☐ 2-4 hours   ☐ other

Listening to music

Listening to music you love will make your brain release more dopamine! The naturally occurring happy chemical. Make sure to listen to more of your favorite tunes!

Meals Today:

Be sure to add Functional Foods in your diet

Breakfast
_____

Snack
_____

Lunch
_____

Snack
_____

Dinner
_____

Snack
_____

Did you Spice up your day with Turmeric?   ☐ yes   ☐ no

(Best for Neuroprotection)

Did you get your Rainbow Greens today?   ☐ yes   ☐ no

(Dark Leafy Green is best for Brain Health)

Did you get Nuts/Seeds today?   ☐ yes   ☐ no

Vitamins I took today _____

(Omega-3 Fatty Acid is best for Your Brain Power and keeping your brain healthy.)
Great Sources of Omega-3s: *Salmon, Oysters, Caviar, Flax Seeds, Chia Seeds, and Walnuts.*
Other Great Sources of Brain Power *– Vitamins: B1, B6, B12, C, E, Antioxidants, Beta Carotene and Probiotics.*

> *Reminder: Cinnamon and Rosemary are great for neurological benefits.*

Daily Exercise:

*If you are at the Beginning of your brain injury recovery, 5 minutes is great on the recumbent bike. OR if you are further along in recovery, a walk, weight bearing exercise and yoga are great choices. Remember not too much. Start slow and build up to 20 minutes. *Consult with your Dr for your proper exercise prescription.*

Exercise Log:

_____
_____
_____
_____

Did you get your Yoga stillness today?   ☐ yes   ☐ no

This is your gateway to mental clarity and spiritual calm. Based on a centuries-old and scientifically proven pathway to health, Yoga is a gold star to your success. Great resources: Glo.com and Asanarebel.com

Daily Reflection:

Date: _____

I am grateful for ...

☀ _____
☀ _____
☀ _____

Positive Affirmations

☀ _____
☀ _____
☀ _____

Did you meditate?　☐ yes　☐ no
(At least 5 minutes, a great meditation APP: Calm.com)

Did you do the following?

Physical Therapy　☐ yes　☐ no

Occupational Therapy　☐ yes　☐ no

Speech Therapy　☐ yes　☐ no

Music Therapy　☐ yes　☐ no

Equine Therapy　☐ yes　☐ no

Cognitive Behavior Therapy ☐ yes　☐ no

How did you feel?

☐ awesome　☐ okay　☐ not so good

Did you get a breath of Fresh Air Today?

☐ yes　☐ no

Did you get your healthy 7-9 hrs of sleep?

☐ yes　☐ no

Naps:

☐ 1-2 hours　☐ 2-4 hours　☐ other

Listening to music

Listening to music you love will make your brain release more dopamine! The naturally occurring happy chemical. Make sure to listen to more of your favorite tunes!

Meals Today:

Be sure to add
Functional Foods in your diet

Breakfast
_____
_____

Snack
_____
_____

Lunch
_____
_____

Snack
_____
_____

Dinner
_____
_____

Snack
_____
_____

Did you Spice up your day with Turmeric? ☐ yes ☐ no
(Best for Neuroprotection)

Did you get your Rainbow Greens today? ☐ yes ☐ no
(Dark Leafy Green is best for Brain Health)

Did you get Nuts/Seeds today? ☐ yes ☐ no

Vitamins I took today _____

(Omega-3 Fatty Acid is best for Your Brain Power and keeping your brain healthy.)
Great Sources of Omega-3s: *Salmon, Oysters, Caviar, Flax Seeds, Chia Seeds, and Walnuts.*
Other Great Sources of Brain Power *– Vitamins: B1, B6, B12, C, E, Antioxidants, Beta Carotene and Probiotics.*

> *Reminder: Cinnamon and Rosemary are great for neurological benefits.*

Daily Exercise:

If you are at the Beginning of your brain injury recovery, 5 minutes is great on the recumbent bike. OR if you are further along in recovery, a walk, weight bearing exercise and yoga are great choices. Remember not too much. Start slow and build up to 20 minutes. *Consult with your Dr for your proper exercise prescription.

Exercise Log:
_____
_____
_____
_____

Did you get your Yoga stillness today? ☐ yes ☐ no

This is your gateway to mental clarity and spiritual calm. Based on a centuries-old and scientifically proven pathway to health, Yoga is a gold star to your success. Great resources: Glo.com and Asanarebel.com

Daily Reflection:

Glossary

Cognitive Behavior Therapy (CBT)

Teaching the TBI Patient healthy ways of thinking. In simple terms, retraining the brain to positively think. It will help identify unhealthy patterns and therefore the patient can then change and find success.

- Brainline.org

Equine Therapy

Typically, equine-assisted therapy is a team effort where a mental health professional works with a horse specialist. Clients who participate in equine-assisted therapy are usually seeking help for emotional or behavioral problems. Clients work with specially trained horses and learn about caring for them.

Benefits:
Increased trust, reduced anxiety, less feeling of depression & isolation, connection to the horse provides emotional stimulation, Increased self-esteem and self-acceptance, better impulse control, works on muscles to develop balance increased problem solving, improved communication skills and can jump start healing.

* **With** a doctor's prescription, it is generally covered by insurance.

Functional Food

A functional food is a food claimed to have an additional function by adding new ingredients or more of existing ingredients. The term may also apply to traits purposely bred into existing edible plants, such as purple or gold potatoes having increased anthocyanin or carotenoid contents, respectively. –Wikipedia

Examples of Functional Food

- Fruits: berries, kiwi, pears, peaches, apples, oranges, bananas
- Vegetables: broccoli, cauliflower, kale, spinach, zucchini
- Nuts: almonds, cashews, pistachios, macadamia nuts, Brazil nuts
- Seeds: chia seeds, flax seeds, hemp seeds, pumpkin seeds
- Legumes: black beans, chickpeas, navy beans, lentils
- Whole grains: oats, barley, buckwheat, brown rice, couscous
- Seafood: salmon, sardines, anchovies, mackerel, cod
- Fermented foods: tempeh, kombucha, kimchi, kefir, sauerkraut
- Herbs and spices: turmeric, cinnamon, ginger, cayenne pepper
- Beverages: coffee, green tea, black tea

Music Therapy

March is Music Therapy Month

interventions demonstrate promising improvement in patient outcomes in rehabilitation, and these effects can be enhanced when facilitated by credentialed music therapists

– Magee, W.L. et al., 2017).

Interventions:

- Songwriting: in which the patient creates lyrics and/or music supported by the therapist
- Playing musical instruments: Therapeutic Instrumental Musical Performance, improvisation, cognitive training
- Listening to patient preferred music (live or recorded), using song choice or lyric discussion

Benefits

- Negative mood states and quality of life
- Cognitive recovery
- Physical performance, including walking, upper limb function and talking
- Communication outcomes, including voice, speech and language Decrease confusion
- Enhance executive functioning (planning and executing tasks?)
- Improve verbal memory
- Increase focused attention
- Improve fine motor dexterity and gross motor function (e.g. gait, upper extremity)
- Improve gait parameters of velocity, stride length, and cadence
- Improve the timing and range of movements
- Improve expressive language
- Improve voice functioning
- Decrease depression
- Improve mood
- Increase quality of life

The American Music Therapy Association Goals *To support cognitive functioning (Särkämö et al., 2008; Siponkoski et al., 2020)*

To improve communication (Hurkmans et al., 2012; Magee, W.L. et al., 2017)

To improve motor functioning (Magee, W.L. et al., 2017; Nascimento et al., 2015; Yoo et al., 2016)

To improve emotional well-being (Magee, W.L. et al., 2017; Särkämö et al., 2008)

Occupational Therapy (OT)

April is National Occupational Therapy Month.

Occupational therapy is a branch of health care that helps people of all ages who have physical, sensory, or cognitive problems. OT can help them regain independence in all areas of their lives. Occupational therapists help with barriers that affect a person's emotional, social, and physical needs.

- www.aota.org

Primary focus is on self-care skills, education, work, or social interaction.

Physical Therapy (PT)

October is National Physical Therapy Month

Physical Therapy is a **medical treatment used to restore functional movements, such as standing, walking, and moving different body parts**. It can be an effective treatment for medical conditions or injuries resulting in pain, movement dysfunction, or limited mobility.

- **www.apta.org**

Traumatic Brain Injury (TBI)

March is Brain Injury Awareness Month

A traumatic brain injury, or TBI, is an injury that affects how the brain works. TBI is a major cause of death and disability in the United States. Anyone can experience a TBI, but data suggest that some groups are at greater risk for getting a TBI or having worse health outcomes after the injury.

- 176 Americans died from TBI-related injury each day in 2020. Total, 64,000.
- 223,000 TBI Hospitalizations in 2019.
- 15% in 2019, about 15% U.S high school students self-reported one or more sports or recreation-related concussions within the preceding 12 months.

  – *Centers for Disease Control and Prevention*

Visit **KristinAbello.com**
to buy the book

Sunrise:
Life after Traumatic Brain Injury:
A Healing Journey
in Surviving TBI,
An Empowering True Story

Wife, Mother, Daughter, Sister and Friend. These are the words best used to describe the force that is Kristin Abello. She and her husband Raul Abello are the parents of two wonderful boys, Jacob (21) and Colin (17) and they currently reside in the city of Houston with their Golden Retrievers Max and Lucy.

On any given day, you can catch Kristin participating in several outdoor activities or maybe just hanging out with her family at the beach. But life hasn't always been so picturesque. What Kristin thought would be a routine run with her husband, turned into an event that rocked Kristin and her family to the core. After being struck by a car, Kristin suffered a severe Traumatic Brain Injury. But with faith, determination and a positive attitude, Kristin has more than survived – she has thrived. The key is not being a victim of circumstance. The impossible is truly possible!

Alongside her beautiful family, Kristins' list of accomplishments includes working at both Halliburton and Texas Children's Hospital, as an Exercise Specialist. Serving on the TIRR (The Institution for Rehabilitation and Research) Family Board, The TIRR Foundation Board (2005-2015), and participating as an Auction Chair and Committee Member of various schools in the Houston Metropolis. She also continues to pioneer the TIRR (2013) and Western Academy (2016) Auction. Alongside her husband, Kristin was awarded the Remembrance Day named Kristin and Raul Abello Day, By Mayor Annis D. Parker of the City of Houston.

Since thriving through her TBI experience, Kristin has made it her life's mission to share her story with the world. She is passionate about changing the narrative of the TBI community from a somber song to more of an upbeat melody. She wants survivors, family and/or friends who have lived through a TBI experience to know that a positive perspective can change even the bleakest of experiences.

Follow Kristin:

KristinAbello.com

Instagram.com/kristin.abello

Facebook.com/itskristinabello

Made in the USA
Coppell, TX
07 November 2022

85897217R00111